Satellite Environment Handbook

Satellite Environment Handbook

Second Edition

Edited by **Francis S. Johnson**

Director, Earth and Planetary Sciences Laboratory
Southwest Center for Advanced Studies
Dallas, Texas

Contributors

A. J. Dessler	H. C. Ko
W. B. Hanson	B. J. O'Brien
F. S. Johnson	James F. Vedder

Stanford University Press, Stanford, California   1965

First edition © 1961 by Lockheed Aircraft Corporation
Second edition © 1965 by the Board of Trustees of the
Leland Stanford Junior University
Printed and bound by Stanford University Press
Stanford, California, U.S.A.
L.C. 64-8894

Preface to the Second Edition

The first edition of this handbook was prepared in response to numerous requests from space engineering projects for the best available data on satellite environment. The time was early in the space age, and information concerning the natural environment had just begun to grow at a very rapid pace. It was recognized therefore that revisions of many of the data presented in the book would be required at an early date.

In the three and a half years that have passed since the preparation of the First Edition, data have poured forth at what might be described as a bewildering rate, and the preparation of the Second Edition has been a more difficult task than was the preparation of the First. Surprisingly enough, only a few of the ideas presented in the First Edition have proved to be incorrect. Even more surprising is the fact that so few of the older concepts have changed. Rather, new concepts and phenomena have simply been added to the old list—for example, the addition of a layer of helium ions to the ionospheric model without significantly altering the other ionospheric parameters, or the addition of a belt of ~ 1 Mev protons to the outer zone of the Van Allen radiation without appreciable alteration of the older flux estimates. Most of the phenomena that had to be described as not understood in the First Edition are still not understood—notably such phenomena as the aurora and the Van Allen radiation belt. The phenomena can now be described more accurately and completely, but the basic causes still escape understanding. One can only hope that such causes will be seen clearly in the next few years.

In this new edition, there are many significant improvements and additions to the description of satellite environment. For example, three model atmospheres are presented to indicate conditions typical of the extremes of the sunspot cycle and an in-between situation, the latter having a density distribution similar to the U.S. Standard Atmosphere 1962 but otherwise having physical parameters thought to be more realistic than those in the Standard Atmosphere. A more detailed description of the upper portion of the ionosphere has been made possible by topside-sounder (Alouette) data and improved theoretical concepts. There is an expanded description of charged-particle motion and magnetic coordinate systems and a more detailed description of the geomagnetically trapped radiation, including the Starfish radiation belt. Many new data in the extreme ultraviolet portion of the solar spectrum have become available and are presented. The data on micrometeorites have been substantially revised on the basis of space probe measurements. The description of radio noise has been completely rewritten, and it now includes the 10.7-cm solar radio noise that has become such an important index of solar ultraviolet emission. The description of geomagnetic activity has been expanded, and a revised picture of the effect of the solar wind on the geomagnetic field is given.

In order to keep the size of this work within reasonable limits, we have attempted to treat each topic as concisely as possible consistent with clarity for use as a handbook. We trust research workers will be forgiving when they find their specialty, which by itself could fill a large volume, condensed to a page or two.

We are, as before, indebted to our many colleagues in the scientific community, and we acknowledge our debt to them for many stimulating discussions on subject matters relating to this handbook. We also appreciate the efficient and rapid handling of the manuscript by the Stanford University Press. Lockheed Missiles and Space Company provided the support for the preparation of the First Edition of this handbook; we are grateful that Lockheed generously released their copyright to the Stanford University Press so that this revised edition could be prepared.

F.S.J.

Dallas, Texas
November 1964

Preface to the First Edition

Data on the elements of the satellite environment are being acquired at a rapid rate, but large gaps in our knowledge of this area still exist and will continue to exist for several years at least. Knowledge in this field is growing so rapidly that we might describe it as an exploding field. Many of the phenomena described in this book were not known or even suspected three years ago. Some of our present ideas will undoubtedly have to be altered in varying degrees within the next year or two. It is probable that there are still some major surprises in store for us.

In such a situation, where our ideas concerning the space environment are developing and changing rapidly, it may appear unwise to attempt to publish a compilation of the existing data. However, there is an urgent need for the best estimates that can be made of the nature of the space environment. These estimates are particularly needed in connection with engineering projects for space systems, but such data are also required in the rapidly developing field of space physics.

The satellite-environment data presented here have been compiled principally in response to numerous questions from engineering projects directed to the Space Physics Research organization at Lockheed Missiles and Space Division. It was also recognized, however, that many research activities should also profit from the organization of data in the several fields of endeavor. Consequently, it is hoped that the data and analyses presented here will be useful in diverse research and engineering programs in space-systems development, in geophysics, in meteorology, and in other disciplines.

The available data describing the geophysical environment encountered by artificial Earth satellites are presented in a comprehensive summary. The major satellite-environment factors—the structure of the upper atmosphere and the ionosphere, penetrating-particle radiation, solar radiation, micrometeorites, radio noise, thermal radiation from Earth, and geomagnetism—are discussed, and existing data are evaluated. An effort has been made to describe these factors completely, even from insufficient experimental data, provided there is a physical basis for extrapolating from whatever data are available. Needless to say, many of the data included will require modification as more measurements are obtained.

We are indebted to our colleagues in the scientific community for many helpful and stimulating discussions on matters relating to the material presented in the book. We are grateful for the use of several figures which have been made available to us by various research groups. Working with the competent staff of the Stanford University Press has been a pleasant and informative experience. It is also a pleasure to acknowledge the assistance of Research Technical Publications at LMSD and in particular José Villarreal, who assisted in the preparation of the technical report upon which this book is based.

F.S.J.

Palo Alto, California
March 1961

Contents

Tables

Illustrations

1. Structure of the Upper Atmosphere

Francis S. Johnson

Southwest Center for Advanced Studies, Dallas

1. Structure of the Upper Atmosphere

Francis S. Johnson

Southwest Center for Advanced Studies, Dallas

1.1. INTRODUCTION

The structure of the lower atmosphere in both position and time has been studied in considerable detail by meteorologists. However, as one examines higher and higher levels it is apparent that fewer and fewer data exist. Nevertheless, considerable information is available concerning the structure of the atmosphere to its outermost fringes. In this paper, we will concentrate attention on the higher levels and almost entirely ignore the region of meteorological interest.

On the basis of thermal structure, the atmosphere is divided into a number of regions. The lowest region, the troposphere, extends to an altitude of about 10 km over the poles and 16 km over the equator; this is the principal region of meteorological interest. The upper boundary of the troposphere is the tropopause. Above the troposphere is the stratosphere, which has the stratopause as its upper boundary. There is some confusion as to the definition of the stratopause, but it is probably most satisfactory to consider it to be the temperature maximum which occurs near 50 km. Above the stratospause is the mesosphere, which extends to the temperature minimum near 80 km. (Frequently, the mesosphere is taken to be the broad region around the temperature maximum rather than just the upper half of it, as is suggested above.) Above the mesopause (the upper boundary of the mesosphere) is the thermosphere, in which the temperature rises rapidly up to about 200-km altitude and less rapidly above 200 km, becoming essentially isothermal above 400 km. Another region which is frequently mentioned is the exosphere, which is the upper portion of the thermosphere and is the region in which the atmospheric gas is so rarefied that collisions between neutral particles can generally be neglected. The altitude of the base of the exosphere varies from 350 to 700 km during the sunspot cycle.

Many model atmospheres have been published; among the most widely used are the ARDC 1959 atmosphere (Air Force Geophysics Research Directorate, 1960) and the U.S. Standard Atmosphere, 1962. The medium density atmosphere presented below is similar to the 1962 Standard Atmosphere in its density distribution, but the physical parameters associated with it are thought to be more realistic than those in the Standard Atmosphere (Johnson, 1962). Two additional model atmospheres (low-density and high-density) are also presented below to typify the near-extreme conditions that occur in the atmosphere.

1.2. ATMOSPHERIC RELATIONSHIPS

Because the sun heats the atmosphere nonuniformly, the physical properties of the atmosphere vary in space and time. Several equations relate these physical properties. Foremost among these is the hydrostatic relationship, which governs the vertical distribution of pressure. In differential form, the hydrostatic relationship is

$$dp = -\rho g dh , \qquad (1\text{-}1)$$

where, at altitude h, p is the pressure, ρ is the atmospheric density, and g is the acceleration of gravity. This equation can also be expressed in the form

$$\frac{dp}{p} = \frac{-mg}{kT} dh = \frac{-dh}{H} , \qquad (1\text{-}2)$$

where m is the average particle mass, T is the temperature at altitude h, k is the Boltzmann constant, and H is the scale height. If m, g, and T are all constant, then H is the vertical distance over which the pressure changes by the factor e (the base of natural logarithms); it is defined by the expression

$$H = kT/mg . \qquad (1\text{-}3)$$

When Eq. (1-2) is integrated, we obtain

$$p/p_0 = \exp\left[-\int_0^h (mg/kT)dh\right], \qquad (1\text{-}4)$$

where p_0 is the pressure at an arbitrarily selected reference level at which h is assigned the value zero. By means of Eq. (1-4) the pressure ratio can be determined for any two levels between which the distributions of temperature and mean particle mass are known.

If the temperature and the average particle mass are constant with altitude, then, neglecting the variation of g with altitude, Eq. (1-4) simplifies to

$$p/p_0 = \exp\left(-h/H\right) = \exp\left(-mgh/kT\right) . \qquad (1\text{-}4')$$

Further, $\rho/\rho_0 = n/n_0 = p/p_0$, where ρ and n are respectively the atmospheric density and particle concentration at altitude h, and ρ_0 and n_0 are the corresponding quantities at the reference level where $h = 0$. When the variation of g with altitude is taken into account we obtain, instead of Eq. (1-4'),

$$p/p_0 = n/n_0 = \rho/\rho_0 = \exp\left[-mg_0 R_0 h/(R_0 + h)kT\right], \qquad (1\text{-}4'')$$

where R_0 is the distance from the center of the Earth to the reference level and g_0 is the acceleration of gravity at the reference level. Equation (1-4″) is one form of the generalized hydrostatic equation.

When the temperature and the average particle mass are not constant with altitude, Eq. (1-4) must be used instead of (1-4′) or (1-4″). The corresponding equations for the density and particle concentration are

$$\rho/\rho_0 = (mT_0/m_0 T) \exp\left[-\int_0^h (mg/kT)dh\right] \tag{1-5}$$

and

$$n/n_0 = (T_0/T) \exp\left[-\int_0^h (mg/kT)dh\right]. \tag{1-6}$$

In Eq. (1-4), (1-5), and (1-6) the variation of temperature and mean particle mass must be known over the altitude region of concern, and the variation in g with altitude should be taken into account by using the relationship

$$g = g_0 R_0^2/(R_0 + h)^2. \tag{1-7}$$

These are the most general forms of the equations expressing the relationships among the physical properties of the atmosphere and altitude.

The pressure may vary horizontally as well as vertically. When a horizontal pressure gradient exists, there is a tendency for the atmosphere to move horizontally in such a way as to equalize the pressure. Because of the rotation of the Earth, there is also a Coriolis force which deflects the movement to such an extent that the pressure-equalization flow is eventually stopped. In this limiting case, a balanced circulation is obtained in which the Coriolis and centrifugal forces associated with the circulation just balance the horizontal-pressure-gradient force. When the centrifugal force of the circulation due to the curvature of the particle trajectories is neglected, the balanced circulation can be computed by equating the Coriolis force to the pressure-gradient force. The wind calculated in this manner is known as the geostrophic wind, and the magnitude of its velocity is given by the equation

$$v = \frac{1}{2\rho\,\Omega\,\sin\lambda} \,|\,\nabla_H p\,|, \tag{1-8}$$

where $|\,\nabla_H p\,|$ is the magnitude of the horizontal pressure gradient, Ω is the angular rate of rotation of the Earth, and λ is the latitude. It can also be expressed in the form

$$v = \frac{gs}{2\,\Omega\,\sin\lambda}, \tag{1-8′}$$

where s is the slope of the constant-pressure surface passing through the point in question. If the air motion is along a curved path, a centrifugal-force term should be added in Eq. (1-8) and the calculated wind, taking this force into account, is known as the gradient wind.

Although pressure differences occur over the Earth, with balanced circulations preventing pressure-equalization winds from annihilating the pressure differences, the variation in pressure at the Earth's surface is not very large. Extreme excursions amount to about ± 5 per cent from the mean (ignoring tornadoes). At altitudes up to 100 km and somewhat above, the pressure distribution and the wind field are related by the gradient-wind equation; from the strength of the observed winds, it is clear that the pressure at given altitudes is relatively constant, although the relative variations are considerably larger than the ± 5 per cent observed at the Earth's surface. At altitudes much in excess of 100 km, viscous forces play a prominent role and tend to prevent balanced circulations from occurring (Johnson, 1960) even though unequal heating must also occur in this altitude range. As a result, pressures are relatively constant over the Earth (i.e., constant within a factor of less than 2) at altitudes near 200 km, because pressure-equalization flows greatly reduce the pressure variations which would otherwise occur.

1.3. ATMOSPHERIC DATA

Atmospheric temperature and pressure are measured directly in the troposphere by using instruments carried aloft with balloons, and the height of the observation is determined by using the hydrostatic equation, Eq. (1-1). However, as one moves well above the troposphere, it becomes difficult to measure temperature directly, because the temperature-measuring elements come into radiative equilibrium with their distant surroundings rather than into conductive equilibrium with their immediate surroundings. Consequently, at the lower rocket altitudes, the common practice is to measure pressure as a function of altitude or to determine the temperature from sound-velocity experiments using grenade sources carried aloft in rockets. Above altitudes of about 100 km, pressure becomes difficult to sense and sound does not propagate well, so density is the quantity more commonly observed as a function of altitude, the measurements generally being made either with vacuum gages which sense gas density or with satellites whose rate of orbital decay is observed.

Atmospheric temperature distributions are shown in **Fig. 1-1** for the extremes of the sunspot cycle and for an average condition approximately in agreement with the density distribution adopted in the 1962 U.S. Standard Atmosphere. Below 100 km, there is no established variation with the sunspot cycle;

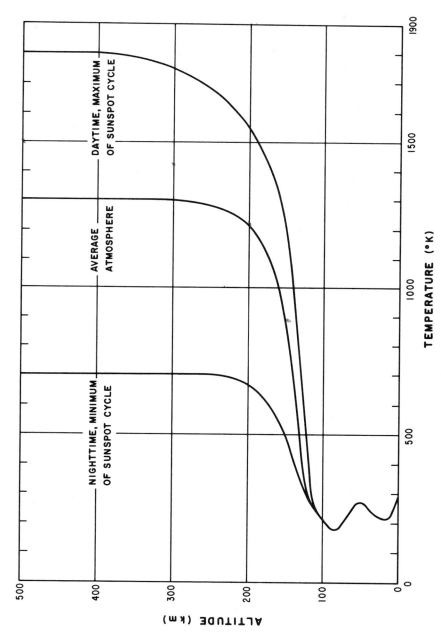

Fig. 1.1. Atmospheric temperature distributions typical of daytime conditions near the maximum of the sunspot cycle, nighttime conditions near the minimum of the sunspot conditions, and an average in-between situation.

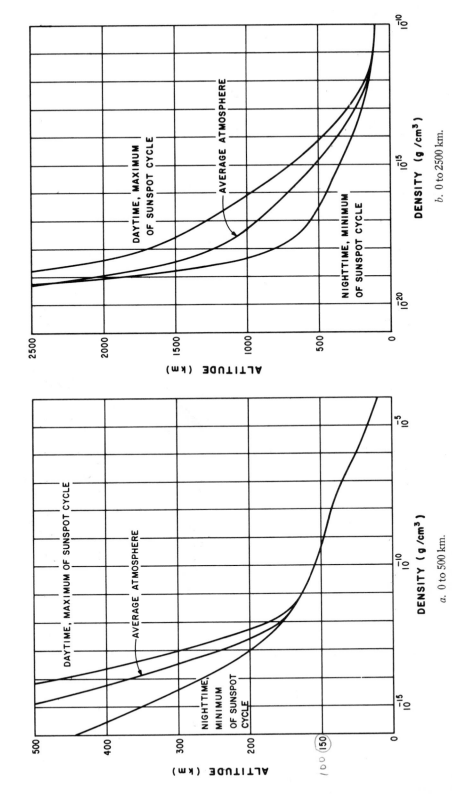

Fig. 1-2. Atmospheric density distributions typical of daytime conditions near the maximum of the sunspot cycle, nighttime conditions near the minimum of the sunspot conditions, and an average in-between situation.

however, there is an appreciable seasonal variation at high altitudes. The lowest temperature distribution in **Fig. 1-1** is typical of nighttime conditions near the minimum of the sunspot cycle, and temperatures much lower than those indicated are not apt to be encountered. The intermediate distribution agrees well with the density distribution selected for the U.S. Standard Atmosphere, 1962 (Johnson, 1962); it corresponds roughly to nighttime conditions near the maximum of the sunspot cycle or to daytime conditions near the middle of the cycle. The highest temperature distribution is typical of daytime conditions near the maximum of the sunspot cycle; higher temperatures are apt to be encountered only when exceptional solar disturbances occur near the maximum of the sunspot cycle. The extreme temperature curves in **Fig. 1-1** are based mainly on deductions from the rates of orbital decay of satellites by Jacchia (1963), Harris and Priester (1963), and Jacchia and Slowey (1964). The sharp rise in temperature between 100 and 200 km and the isothermal distribution above 300 or 400 km are in accordance with a theory originally put forth by Spitzer (1952) and further developed by Bates (1951) and Johnson (1956, 1958). More recently, other researchers have also adopted this concept on theoretical grounds (Nicolet, 1960), or on the basis of experimental evidence (Kallmann, 1961). The isothermal conditions shown in the upper portions of the curves in **Fig. 1-1** apply up to altitudes of several thousand kilometers, beyond which the average particle energy drops because some of the more energetic particles escape from the atmosphere.

Density data for selected conditions are shown in **Fig. 1-2** for the altitude ranges 0 to 500 km and 0 to 2500 km. Three curves are shown, one for daytime conditions near the maximum of the sunspot cycle, one for nighttime conditions near the minimum of the cycle, and one for an average atmosphere that closely approximates the U.S. Standard Atmosphere, 1962.

The concentrations of the various atmospheric constituents near the extremes of the sunspot cycle are shown in **Fig. 1-3**. Concentrations which, when combined with the middle temperature distribution in **Fig. 1-1**, are in good agreement with the density distribution adopted for the U.S. Standard Atmosphere, 1962, are shown in **Fig. 1-4**. There is considerable quantitative uncertainty concerning the composition of the upper atmosphere. However, it is clear that diffusion proceeds rapidly enough at high levels so that diffusive equilibrium in the gravitational field tends to prevail above some altitude. The presence of helium as a principal atmospheric constituent at altitudes above 1500 km near sunspot maximum, first recognized by Nicolet (1961), indicates that diffusive equilibrium distributions must prevail down to altitudes of the order of 105 km, at least for some constituents. The first mass-spectroscopic measurements indicating the presence of diffusive equilibrium between argon and nitrogen above approxi-

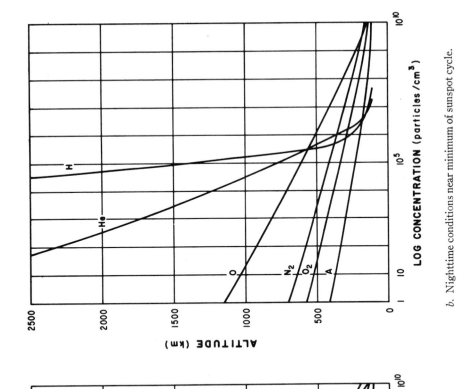

a. Daytime conditions near maximum of sunspot cycle.

b. Nighttime conditions near minimum of sunspot cycle.

Fig. 1-3. Concentrations of major atmospheric constituents.

mately 110-km altitude were those of Meadows and Townsend (1960). Direct measurements of molecular oxygen (Byram *et al.*, 1955), of atomic and molecular oxygen (Schaefer, 1963), and of atmospheric composition (Nier *et al.*, 1964) also provide useful information indicating that diffusive equilibrium distributions prevail above about 105-km altitude. In the presence of diffusive equilibrium, each constituent is distributed independently of the others, and the vertical distribution of each component is just that which would prevail with the temperature distributions shown in **Fig. 1-1** with all the other constituents absent. Consequently, the shape of each of the curves shown can be calculated individually, using the hydrostatic equation.

The atomic hydrogen concentrations around the Earth have been determined spectroscopically near the maximum of the sunspot cycle (Purcell and Tousey, 1960). Near the middle of the cycle, Hanson *et al.* (1963) have determined the

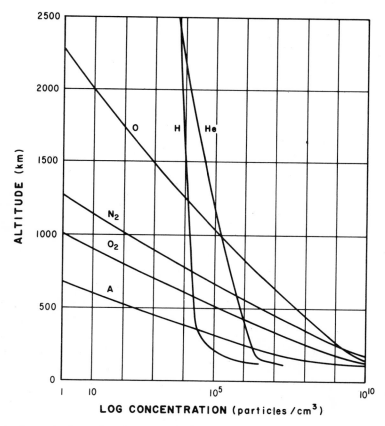

Fig. 1-4. Concentrations of major atmospheric constituents for an exospheric temperature of 1300°K.

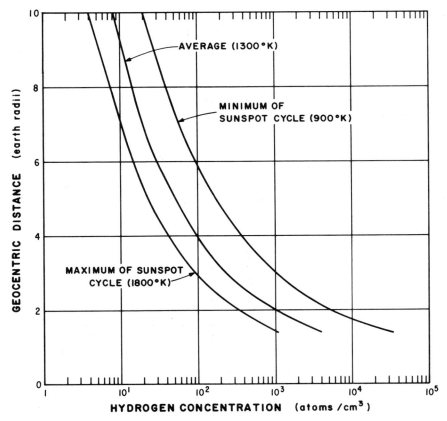

Fig. 1-5. Distributions of atomic hydrogen for daytime conditions near the maximum of the sunspot cycle, near the minimum of the sunspot cycle, and at an average in-between situation.

concentration at 500-km altitude from ion measurements made by Taylor *et al.* (1963) ; the concentration is higher than that indicated by the measurements of Purcell and Tousey. Near sunspot-cycle minimum, the concentrations must be still higher, as indicated in **Figs. 1-3** and **1-4**. The reason for the increase near the sunspot minimum is that the rate of supply of atomic hydrogen into the atmosphere, and hence its rate of escape from the atmosphere, is nearly constant through the sunspot cycle. However, near sunspot minimum, the upper atmosphere is cooler and greater concentrations of atomic hydrogen must build up in order to maintain a constant escape flux. Hanson and Patterson (1963) have shown that the diurnal variations in the hydrogen-atom concentrations are relatively small and that the nighttime concentrations as well as the daytime are controlled mainly by the maximum daytime temperature attained in the upper thermosphere. The hydrogen-atom concentration shown in **Fig. 1-3b**, which applies for a nighttime temperature of about 700 °K, appropriate near sunspot minimum, was calculated on the basis of a temperature of 930 °K, which would be the approximate temperature maximum reached during the daytime. The hydrogen concentrations in **Figs. 1-3a** and **1-4** were determined on the basis of 1800 and 1300 °K temperatures, since these curves represent daytime conditions. The hydrogen distributions below 400 km differ substantially from diffusive equilibrium distributions, because of the diffusive flow of hydrogen upward through the atmosphere (Bates and Patterson, 1961).

The atomic hydrogen concentrations expected farther from the Earth are shown in **Fig. 1-5**. The concentrations shown are based on the concept that only an insignificant number of atoms are in orbit around the Earth compared with the number moving up from the base of the exosphere on ballistic orbits. The possibility exists that the actual concentrations may be significantly higher than shown (for example, a factor of 3 at 5 Earth radii) if substantial numbers of atoms remain in orbit; however, the probability of ionization by sunlight seems

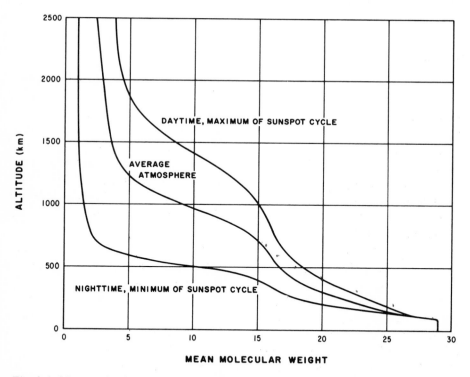

Fig. 1-6. Mean molecular weight distribution typical of daytime conditions near the maximum of the sunspot cycle, nighttime conditions near the minimum of the sunspot conditions, and an average in-between situation.

to make this unlikely. Although the concentrations in the lower exosphere are greater near sunspot minimum than near sunspot maximum, the concentration falls more rapidly with altitude with the lower temperature which prevails near sunspot minimum, therefore the concentrations at distances beyond 5 Earth radii are more constant through the sunspot cycle than are the concentrations in the lower exosphere.

The mean molecular weight of the upper atmosphere is shown as a function of altitude up to 2500 km in **Fig. 1-6**. The sudden decrease in molecular weight that occurs near 500 km at sunspot minimum and 1400 km at sunspot maximum is due to the presence of atomic hydrogen and helium in the atmosphere. Below 100 km, the molecular weight rapidly approaches the value 29.0 that is applicable below 80 km.

Some selected values of atmospheric parameters are shown in Tables 1-1, 1-2, and 1-3 for the low-, medium-, and high-density atmospheres described by **Figs. 1-1** through **1-6**. The scale height, pressure, total particle concentration, and concentrations of molecular nitrogen and atomic and molecular oxygen are also given.

1.4. ATMOSPHERIC VARIATIONS

It is recognized that the atmosphere is dynamic and that changes in it occur frequently. The variations that occur are of several types, associated with the sunspot cycle, diurnal effects, solar activity, magnetic activity, and season.

The sunspot cycle variation has already been described, at least to the extent that its approximate limits have been indicated. It is the largest of the variations, and it is presumably due to variations in the extreme ultraviolet output of the sun. The long-term variation in exospheric temperature as indicated by Jacchia and Slowey (1964) is shown in **Fig. 1-7**; daytime maximum and nighttime minimum temperatures are shown as functions of the 27-day average value of the 10.7-cm radio noise flux from the sun. This noise flux, which is a useful indicator of solar activity, varies from about 70×10^{-22} w/m²-cps near the minimum of the sunspot cycle up to about 250 near the maximum (see **Fig. 6-3**).

The next largest variation is probably the diurnal variation. Jacchia and Slowey (1964) indicate that the daytime maximum in the exospheric temperature is 1.33 times the nighttime minimum. The maximum temperature occurs at about 1400 hours local time; i.e., the maximum lags about 30° behind the sun in longitude. The minimum, which is much flatter than the maximum, occurs at about 0500 hours local time. The diurnal bulge is nearly symmetrical, and it apparently follows the sun in latitude. The polar regions have not been well explored, but it is clear that the atmospheric density there is quite comparable with

TABLE 1-1

Atmospheric Parameters as a Function of Altitude for a Low-Density Atmosphere (Nighttime Near Sunspot Minimum)

The temperature T, particle concentration n, density ρ, pressure p, molecular weight M, scale height H, atomic oxygen concentration $n(O)$, molecular oxygen concentration $n(O_2)$, and molecular nitrogen concentration $n(N_2)$, are given as functions of altitude h.

h (km)	T (°K)	n (particles/cm³)	ρ (g/cm³)	p (dyne/cm²)	M	H (km)	$n(O)$ (particles/cm³)	$n(O_2)$ (particles/cm³)	$n(N_2)$ (particles/cm³)
105	224	4.59×10^{12}	2.14×10^{-10}	1.42×10^{-1}	28.07	7.00	2.80×10^{11}	7.93×10^{11}	3.48×10^{12}
110	243	2.14×10^{12}	9.86×10^{-11}	7.18×10^{-2}	27.73	7.69	1.74×10^{11}	3.34×10^{11}	1.62×10^{12}
120	290	5.51×10^{11}	2.47×10^{-11}	2.20×10^{-2}	26.96	9.47	7.33×10^{10}	7.04×10^{10}	4.05×10^{11}
130	350	1.76×10^{11}	7.64×10^{-12}	8.51×10^{-3}	26.12	11.84	3.42×10^{10}	1.85×10^{10}	1.23×10^{11}
140	425	6.83×10^{10}	2.87×10^{-12}	4.01×10^{-3}	25.27	14.90	1.76×10^{10}	5.98×10^{9}	4.46×10^{10}
150	490	3.21×10^{10}	1.30×10^{-12}	2.17×10^{-3}	24.45	17.81	1.03×10^{10}	2.36×10^{9}	1.94×10^{10}
160	548	1.71×10^{10}	6.70×10^{-13}	1.29×10^{-3}	23.66	20.65	6.52×10^{9}	1.05×10^{9}	9.46×10^{9}
180	625	6.25×10^{9}	2.30×10^{-13}	5.39×10^{-4}	22.19	25.26	3.11×10^{9}	2.74×10^{8}	2.86×10^{9}
200	664	2.80×10^{9}	9.71×10^{-14}	2.57×10^{-4}	20.87	28.71	1.69×10^{9}	8.55×10^{7}	1.03×10^{9}
220	688	1.40×10^{9}	4.57×10^{-14}	1.33×10^{-4}	19.72	31.67	9.66×10^{8}	2.90×10^{7}	3.97×10^{8}
240	699	7.47×10^{8}	2.33×10^{-14}	7.21×10^{-5}	18.77	34.02	5.73×10^{8}	1.04×10^{7}	1.61×10^{8}
260	700	4.21×10^{8}	1.26×10^{-14}	4.07×10^{-5}	17.99	35.75	3.47×10^{8}	3.82×10^{6}	6.72×10^{7}
280	700	2.43×10^{8}	7.02×10^{-15}	2.35×10^{-5}	17.38	37.24	2.12×10^{8}	1.42×10^{6}	2.82×10^{7}
300	700	1.44×10^{8}	4.02×10^{-15}	1.39×10^{-5}	16.89	38.55	1.29×10^{8}	5.29×10^{5}	1.19×10^{7}
350	700	4.11×10^{7}	1.09×10^{-15}	3.97×10^{-6}	15.97	41.37	3.82×10^{7}	4.61×10^{4}	1.41×10^{6}
400	700	1.28×10^{7}	3.19×10^{-16}	1.24×10^{-6}	14.99	44.73	1.15×10^{7}	4.17×10^{3}	1.72×10^{5}
450	700	4.46×10^{6}	9.88×10^{-17}	4.31×10^{-7}	13.33	51.06	3.51×10^{6}	3.91×10^{2}	2.16×10^{4}
500	700	1.85×10^{6}	3.26×10^{-17}	1.79×10^{-7}	10.61	65.11	1.09×10^{6}	3.79×10^{1}	2.81×10^{3}
600	700	6.34×10^{5}	5.07×10^{-18}	6.13×10^{-8}	4.82	147.60	1.11×10^{5}	3.93×10^{-1}	5.16×10^{1}
700	700	3.93×10^{5}	1.67×10^{-18}	3.80×10^{-8}	2.55	286.40	1.21×10^{4}	4.65×10^{-3}	1.06×10
800	700	2.93×10^{5}	9.37×10^{-19}	2.83×10^{-8}	1.93	390.41	1.40×10^{3}	6.22×10^{-5}	2.44×10^{-2}
900	700	2.32×10^{5}	6.36×10^{-19}	2.24×10^{-8}	1.65	468.71	1.72×10^{2}	9.36×10^{-7}	6.20×10^{-4}
1000	700	1.90×10^{5}	4.64×10^{-19}	1.84×10^{-8}	1.47	540.85	2.23×10^{1}	1.58×10^{-8}	1.74×10^{-5}
1500	700	9.20×10^{4}	1.67×10^{-19}	8.89×10^{-9}	1.09	829.94	1.80×10^{-3}	1.02×10^{-16}	1.19×10^{-12}
2000	700	5.34×10^{4}	9.04×10^{-20}	5.16×10^{-9}	1.02	1004.78	4.45×10^{-7}	6.27×10^{-24}	5.83×10^{-19}
2500	700	3.35×10^{4}	5.60×10^{-20}	3.24×10^{-9}	1.00	1144.91	2.81×10^{-10}	2.50×10^{-30}	1.46×10^{-24}

TABLE 1-2

Atmospheric Parameters as a Function of Altitude for a Medium-Density Atmosphere

The temperature T, particle concentration n, density ρ, pressure p, molecular weight M, scale height H, atomic oxygen concentration $n(O)$, molecular oxygen concentration $n(O_2)$, and molecular nitrogen concentration $n(N_2)$, are given as functions of altitude h.

h (km)	T (°K)	n (particles/cm³)	ρ (g/cm³)	p (dyne/cm²)	M	H (km)	$n(O)$ (particles/cm³)	$n(O_2)$ (particles/cm³)	$n(N_2)$ (particles/cm³)
105	224	4.59×10^{12}	2.14×10^{-10}	1.42×10^{-1}	28.07	7.00	2.80×10^{11}	7.93×10^{11}	3.48×10^{12}
110	245	2.13×10^{12}	9.80×10^{-11}	7.20×10^{-2}	27.73	7.76	1.73×10^{11}	3.33×10^{11}	1.61×10^{12}
120	295	5.47×10^{11}	2.45×10^{-11}	2.23×10^{-2}	26.97	9.63	7.25×10^{10}	7.01×10^{10}	4.02×10^{11}
130	466	1.51×10^{11}	6.58×10^{-12}	9.71×10^{-3}	26.25	15.68	2.79×10^{10}	1.64×10^{10}	1.06×10^{11}
140	693	6.09×10^{10}	2.60×10^{-12}	5.82×10^{-3}	25.71	23.88	1.37×10^{10}	5.86×10^{9}	4.12×10^{10}
150	880	3.33×10^{10}	1.40×10^{-12}	4.05×10^{-3}	25.28	30.94	8.57×10^{9}	2.92×10^{9}	2.18×10^{10}
160	997	2.18×10^{10}	9.00×10^{-13}	3.00×10^{-3}	24.89	35.70	6.25×10^{9}	1.76×10^{9}	1.37×10^{10}
180	1140	1.14×10^{10}	4.58×10^{-13}	1.80×10^{-3}	24.17	42.30	3.91×10^{9}	7.90×10^{8}	6.70×10^{9}
200	1213	6.85×10^{9}	2.67×10^{-13}	1.15×10^{-3}	23.47	46.63	2.72×10^{9}	4.06×10^{8}	3.72×10^{9}
220	1251	4.39×10^{9}	1.66×10^{-13}	7.58×10^{-4}	22.78	49.85	1.98×10^{9}	2.22×10^{8}	2.18×10^{9}
240	1275	2.91×10^{9}	1.07×10^{-13}	5.13×10^{-4}	22.11	52.68	1.47×10^{9}	1.25×10^{8}	1.32×10^{9}
260	1286	1.99×10^{9}	7.10×10^{-14}	3.54×10^{-4}	21.44	55.11	1.11×10^{9}	7.17×10^{7}	8.09×10^{8}
280	1294	1.39×10^{9}	4.80×10^{-14}	2.48×10^{-4}	20.81	57.48	8.43×10^{8}	4.16×10^{7}	5.02×10^{8}
300	1299	9.83×10^{8}	3.30×10^{-14}	1.76×10^{-4}	20.21	59.77	6.43×10^{8}	2.43×10^{7}	3.14×10^{8}
350	1300	4.41×10^{8}	1.38×10^{-14}	7.90×10^{-5}	18.91	64.88	3.33×10^{8}	6.54×10^{6}	9.94×10^{7}
400	1300	2.09×10^{8}	6.23×10^{-15}	3.76×10^{-5}	17.92	69.52	1.75×10^{8}	1.79×10^{6}	3.20×10^{7}
450	1300	1.04×10^{8}	2.97×10^{-15}	1.87×10^{-5}	17.19	73.55	9.23×10^{7}	5.01×10^{5}	1.05×10^{7}
500	1300	5.36×10^{7}	1.48×10^{-15}	9.62×10^{-6}	16.66	76.99	4.92×10^{7}	1.42×10^{5}	3.50×10^{6}
600	1300	1.54×10^{7}	4.05×10^{-16}	2.76×10^{-6}	15.90	83.04	1.44×10^{7}	1.22×10^{4}	4.06×10^{5}
700	1300	4.82×10^{6}	1.21×10^{-16}	8.65×10^{-7}	15.09	89.99	4.36×10^{6}	1.12×10^{3}	5.02×10^{4}
800	1300	1.68×10^{6}	3.85×10^{-17}	3.02×10^{-7}	13.80	101.26	1.36×10^{6}	1.09×10^{2}	6.58×10^{3}
900	1300	6.79×10^{5}	1.32×10^{-17}	1.22×10^{-7}	11.74	122.29	4.41×10^{5}	1.14×10^{1}	9.11×10^{2}
1000	1300	3.30×10^{5}	5.05×10^{-18}	5.93×10^{-8}	9.20	160.42	1.47×10^{5}	1.27×10	1.33×10^{2}
1500	1300	5.95×10^{4}	3.57×10^{-19}	1.07×10^{-8}	3.61	465.77	9.16×10^{2}	4.94×10^{-5}	1.84×10^{-2}
2000	1300	2.40×10^{4}	1.17×10^{-19}	4.31×10^{-9}	2.93	648.58	1.05×10^{1}	6.46×10^{-9}	7.38×10^{-6}
2500	1300	1.24×10^{4}	4.91×10^{-20}	2.23×10^{-9}	2.38	896.66	1.98×10^{-1}	2.31×10^{-12}	7.13×10^{-9}

TABLE 1-3

Atmospheric Parameters as a Function of Altitude for a High-Density Atmosphere (Daytime Near Sunspot Maximum)

The temperature T, particle concentration n, density ρ, pressure p, molecular weight M, scale height H, atomic oxygen concentration $n(O)$, molecular oxygen concentration $n(O_2)$, and molecular nitrogen concentration $n(N_2)$ are given as functions of altitude h.

h (km)	T (°K)	n (particles/cm³)	ρ (g/cm³)	p (dyne/cm²)	M	H (km)	$n(O)$ (particles/cm³)	$n(O_2)$ (particles/cm³)	$n(N_2)$ (particles/cm³)
105	224	4.59×10^{12}	2.14×10^{-10}	1.42×10^{-1}	28.07	7.00	2.80×10^{11}	7.93×10^{11}	3.48×10^{12}
110	246	2.12×10^{12}	9.78×10^{-11}	7.21×10^{-2}	27.73	7.79	1.73×10^{11}	3.32×10^{11}	1.60×10^{12}
120	435	4.41×10^{11}	1.98×10^{-11}	2.65×10^{-2}	27.10	14.14	5.44×10^{10}	5.83×10^{10}	3.26×10^{11}
130	705	1.58×10^{11}	7.00×10^{-12}	1.54×10^{-2}	26.67	23.35	2.43×10^{10}	1.88×10^{10}	1.14×10^{11}
140	985	7.90×10^{10}	3.46×10^{-12}	1.07×10^{-2}	26.35	33.12	1.40×10^{10}	8.76×10^{9}	5.61×10^{10}
150	1190	5.00×10^{10}	2.16×10^{-12}	8.21×10^{-3}	26.08	40.55	9.84×10^{9}	5.22×10^{9}	3.48×10^{10}
160	1324	3.56×10^{10}	1.53×10^{-12}	6.51×10^{-3}	25.84	45.69	7.67×10^{9}	3.52×10^{9}	2.44×10^{10}
180	1455	2.15×10^{10}	9.05×10^{-13}	4.32×10^{-3}	25.36	51.46	5.40×10^{9}	1.92×10^{9}	1.41×10^{10}
200	1545	1.39×10^{10}	5.76×10^{-13}	2.97×10^{-3}	24.88	56.03	4.01×10^{9}	1.12×10^{9}	8.79×10^{9}
220	1605	9.50×10^{9}	3.85×10^{-13}	2.11×10^{-3}	24.40	59.71	3.08×10^{9}	6.91×10^{8}	5.72×10^{9}
240	1656	6.65×10^{9}	2.64×10^{-13}	1.52×10^{-3}	23.92	63.24	2.41×10^{9}	4.35×10^{8}	3.80×10^{9}
260	1690	4.79×10^{9}	1.86×10^{-13}	1.12×10^{-3}	23.43	66.28	1.92×10^{9}	2.81×10^{8}	2.58×10^{9}
280	1721	3.50×10^{9}	1.33×10^{-13}	8.31×10^{-4}	22.94	69.35	1.54×10^{9}	1.84×10^{8}	1.78×10^{9}
300	1745	2.60×10^{9}	9.70×10^{-14}	6.27×10^{-4}	22.46	72.27	1.24×10^{9}	1.22×10^{8}	1.24×10^{9}
350	1785	1.31×10^{9}	4.64×10^{-14}	3.24×10^{-4}	21.29	79.14	7.48×10^{8}	4.52×10^{7}	5.19×10^{8}
400	1799	7.09×10^{8}	2.38×10^{-14}	1.76×10^{-4}	20.21	85.27	4.64×10^{8}	1.75×10^{7}	2.26×10^{8}
450	1800	4.02×10^{8}	1.29×10^{-14}	9.98×10^{-5}	19.27	90.81	2.93×10^{8}	6.98×10^{6}	1.01×10^{8}
500	1800	2.35×10^{8}	7.22×10^{-15}	5.85×10^{-5}	18.48	96.08	1.86×10^{8}	2.82×10^{6}	4.57×10^{7}
600	1800	8.73×10^{7}	2.51×10^{-15}	2.17×10^{-5}	17.33	105.49	7.65×10^{7}	4.77×10^{5}	9.66×10^{6}
700	1800	3.50×10^{7}	9.65×10^{-16}	8.70×10^{-6}	16.59	113.33	3.23×10^{7}	8.49×10^{4}	2.13×10^{6}
800	1800	1.49×10^{7}	3.97×10^{-16}	3.70×10^{-6}	16.08	120.30	1.40×10^{7}	1.59×10^{4}	4.91×10^{5}
900	1800	6.63×10^{6}	1.72×10^{-16}	1.65×10^{-6}	15.61	127.41	6.17×10^{6}	3.10×10^{3}	1.18×10^{5}
1000	1800	3.10×10^{6}	7.73×10^{-17}	7.70×10^{-7}	15.04	135.90	2.79×10^{6}	6.34×10^{2}	2.94×10^{4}
1500	1800	1.84×10^{5}	2.63×10^{-18}	4.57×10^{-8}	8.61	270.46	7.13×10^{4}	4.14×10^{-1}	4.80×10^{1}
2000	1800	5.41×10^{4}	4.04×10^{-19}	1.34×10^{-8}	4.50	585.20	2.82×10^{3}	6.50×10^{-4}	1.69×10^{-1}
2500	1800	2.60×10^{4}	1.66×10^{-19}	6.45×10^{-9}	3.86	766.96	1.61×10^{2}	2.11×10^{-6}	1.12×10^{-3}

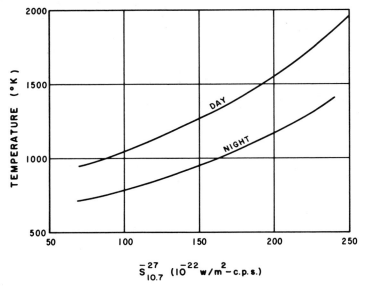

Fig. 1-7. Average daytime and nighttime exospheric temperatures shown as functions of the 27-day average of the 10.7-cm solar radio-noise flux.

that at lower latitudes, probably resembling nighttime conditions. The diurnal variation in temperature appears to result from the sun's ultraviolet radiation.

More or less random variations in exospheric temperature occur from day to day, and the daily value of the 10.7-cm solar radio noise flux is a useful indicator of the magnitude of these variations. **Figure 1-7** indicates the variation of exospheric temperature with solar radio noise for long-term variations; the short-term variations are not as marked (Jacchia, 1963). Whereas the slope of the nighttime curve given in **Fig. 1-7** is $dT/ds = 4.5$, the short-term variations are better described by a slope equal to 2.5. Thus, the average temperature during a 27-day period can be determined by using **Fig. 1-7**, and the temperature on any given day can be estimated by correcting the temperature obtained from **Fig. 1-7** by the amount

$$\Delta T = 2.5(S - \overline{S}) , \tag{1-9}$$

where $\overline{S}$ is the 27-day average value of the 10.7-cm solar radio noise flux and S is the value for the day in question. These day-to-day variations probably result from variations in the solar ultraviolet radiation.

The exospheric temperature also varies with magnetic activity. Jacchia and Slowey (1964) indicate that the temperature increase at low latitudes is numerically equal to the planetary a_p index, but that over the winter polar region the temperature increase is 4 or 5 times as large. These variations probably result from the absorption of hydromagnetic-wave energy (Dessler, 1959; Francis and Karplus, 1960), although energetic charged particles may also play a role in heating the polar zones where the effect is most pronounced.

Annual and semi-annual variations in exospheric temperature have been observed (Paetzold, 1963). Of these two, the semi-annual variation is the more clearly established; its amplitude is about 200 °K near the maximum of the sunspot cycle and about half as great near the minimum; the semi-annual maxima occur in early April and October. The annual variation has its maximum in January and its minimum in July. The cause of these effects is not fully understood. Geomagnetic activity undergoes a semi-annual variation that agrees in phase with the atmospheric variation, but the atmospheric variation is too large to be regarded as resulting from the magnetic. The annual variation is in phase with the varying distance from the Earth to the sun, but again the effect is too large to be explained in this way.

REFERENCES

Air Force Geophysics Research Directorate. 1960. *Handbook of Geophysics.* Macmillan, pp. 1–1 to 1–43.

Bates, D. R. 1951. "The Temperature of the Upper Atmosphere," *Proc. Phys. Soc. (London), B,* **64**, 805–21.

Bates, D. R., and T. N. L. Patterson. 1961. "Hydrogen Atoms and Ions in the Thermosphere and Exosphere," *Planet. Space Sci.,* **5**, 257–73.

Byram, E. T., T. A. Chubb, and H. Friedman. 1955. "Dissociation of Oxygen in the Upper Atmosphere," *Phys. Rev.,* **98**, 1594–97.

Dessler, A. J. 1959. "Upper Atmosphere Density Variations Due to Hydromagnetic Heating," *Nature,* **184**, 261–62.

Francis, W. E., and R. Karplus. 1960. "Hydromagnetic Waves in the Ionosphere," *J. Geophys. Research,* **65**, 3593–3600.

Hanson, W. B., and T. N. L. Patterson. 1963. "Diurnal Variation of Hydrogen Concentration in the Exosphere," *Planet. Space Sci.,* **11**, 1035–52.

Hanson, W. B., T. N. L. Patterson, and S. S. Degaonkar. 1963. "Some Deductions from a Measurement of the Hydrogen Ion Distribution in the High Atmosphere," *J. Geophys. Research,* **68**, 6203–5.

Harris, I., and W. Priester. 1963. "Heating of the Upper Atmosphere," in W. Priester, ed., *Space Research III.* North-Holland Publishing Co., Amsterdam, pp. 53–75.

Jacchia, L. G. 1963. "Electromagnetic and Corpuscular Heating of the Upper Atmosphere," in W. Priester, ed., *Space Research III.* North-Holland Publishing Co., Amsterdam, pp. 3–18.

Jacchia, L. G., and J. Slowey. 1964. "Atmospheric Heating in the Auroral Zones: A Preliminary Analysis of the Atmospheric Drag of the Injun 3 Satellite," *J. Geophys. Research,* **69**, 905–10.

Johnson, F. S. 1956. "Temperature Distribution of the Ionosphere under Control of Thermal Conductivity," *J. Geophys. Research,* **61**, 71–76.

Johnson, F. S. 1958. "Temperatures in the High Atmosphere," *Ann. Geophys.,* **14**, 94–108.

Johnson, F. S. 1960. "Pressure and Temperature Equalization at 200-km Altitude," *J. Geophys. Research,* **65,** 2227–32.

Johnson, F. S. 1962. "Atmospheric Structure," *Astronautics,* **7,** No. 8, 54–61.

Kallmann Bijl, H. K. 1961. "Daytime and Nighttime Atmospheric Properties Derived from Rocket and Satellite Observations," *J. Geophys. Research,* **66,** 787–95.

Meadows, E. B., and J. W. Townsend. 1960. "IGY Rocket Measurements of Arctic Atmospheric Composition above 100 km," in H. Kallmann Bijl, ed., *Space Research.* North-Holland Publishing Co., Amsterdam, pp. 175–98.

Nicolet, M. 1960. "Les variations de la densité et du transport de chaleur par conduction dans l'atmosphère supérieure," in H. Kallmann Bijl, ed., *Space Research.* North-Holland Publishing Co., Amsterdam, pp. 46–89.

Nicolet, M. 1961. "Helium, an Important Constituent in the Lower Exosphere," *J. Geophys. Research,* **68,** 2263–64.

Nier, A. O., J. H. Hoffman, C. Y. Johnson, and J. C. Holmes. 1964. "Neutral Composition of the Atmosphere in the 100- to 200-Kilometer Range," *J. Geophys. Research,* **69,** 979–89.

Paetzold, H. K. 1963. "Solar Activity Effects in the Upper Atmosphere Deduced from Satellite Observations," in W. Priester, ed., *Space Research III.* North-Holland Publishing Co., Amsterdam, pp. 28–52.

Purcell, J. D., and R. Tousey. 1960. "The Profile of Solar Hydrogen-Lyman-α," *J. Geophys. Research,* **65,** 370–72.

Schaefer, E. J. 1963. "The Dissociation of Oxygen Measured by a Rocket-Borne Mass Spectrometer," *J. Geophys. Research,* **68,** 1175–76.

Spitzer, L., Jr. 1952. "The Terrestrial Atmosphere above 300 km," in G. P. Kuiper, ed., *Atmospheres of the Earth and Planets.* University of Chicago Press, pp. 211–47.

Taylor, H. A., Jr., L. H. Brace, H. C. Brinton, and C. R. Smith. 1963. "Direct Measurements of Helium and Hydrogen Ion Concentrations and Total Ion Density to an Altitude of 940 Kilometers," *J. Geophys. Research,* **68,** 5339–47.

2. Structure of the Ionosphere

W. B. Hanson

Southwest Center for Advanced Studies, Dallas

2. Structure of the Ionosphere

W. B. Hanson

Southwest Center for Advanced Studies, Dallas

2.1. INTRODUCTION

The radiation from the sun contains sufficient energy at short wavelengths to cause appreciable photo-ionization of the Earth's atmosphere at high altitudes. Thus the sun's radiation gives rise in the upper atmosphere to a partially ionized region known as the ionosphere. The recombination of the ions and electrons which are produced in this manner proceeds slowly enough at the low gas densities involved so that fairly high concentrations of electrons persist even throughout the night. During the daytime, several distinct ionospheric "layers" or "regions" are recognized, although the separation between them is not as distinct as was originally believed. In order of increasing altitude and increasing ion concentration, they are called the D, E, F_1, and F_2 regions. The different regions are identified in **Fig. 2-1**, which shows typical daytime and nighttime electron distributions as functions of altitude for the extremes of the sunspot cycle. The data apply for geomagnetic latitudes near 30 or 40 deg. Above the maximum electron concentration in the F_2 region, the electron concentration decreases monotonically out to several Earth radii, where the Earth's magnetic field and the protonosphere (the outermost portion of the ionosphere) are terminated by the solar wind or interplanetary plasma. Large diurnal effects occur, particularly in the lower ionosphere; these can be seen by comparing the daytime and nighttime curves in **Fig. 2-1**. The F_1 and F_2 regions join at night, and a valley, or depression in electron concentration, appears between the E and F regions. The D region electron concentrations also decrease drastically at night. The dependence of electron concentration on latitude is rather complicated and is not completely known or understood. Generally recognized features of this dependence will be described in the following discussions of the individual regions.

The electron concentration is essentially equal to the ion concentration everywhere in the ionosphere. There is an exception to this equality in the D region, where electrons may combine with molecules to form negative ions (negative ions are of no importance elsewhere in the ionosphere). Otherwise, throughout

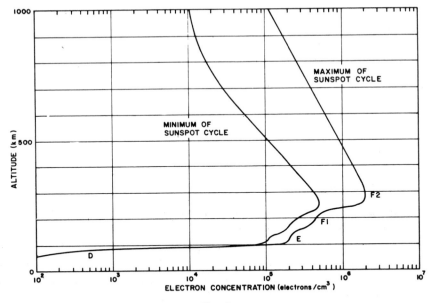

a. Daytime.

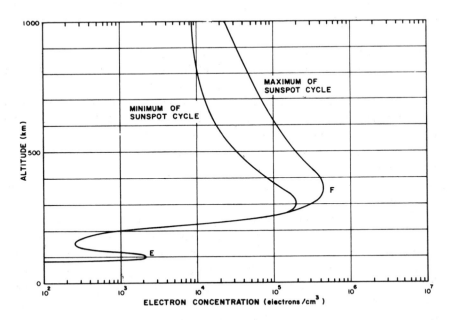

b. Nighttime.

Fig. 2-1. Normal electron distributions at the extremes of the sunspot cycle.

the ionosphere, the ion and electron concentrations are equal because they are created in pairs and eliminated in pairs. Electric forces prevent any significant difference in concentration from developing between positive and negative particles. The ions and electrons may have different drift velocities, however, and this condition gives rise to ionospheric currents.

There is a generally accepted nomenclature for the properties of the different ionospheric regions—N_mD, N_mE, N_mF$_1$, and N_mF$_2$ denote the maximum electron concentrations in the D, E, F$_1$, and F$_2$ regions, respectively; h_mD, h_mE, h_mF$_1$ and h_mF$_2$ denote the heights of the peak concentrations in the various regions; and fD, fE, fF$_1$, and fF$_2$ are the critical frequencies for the peak electron concentrations, i.e., they are the lowest radio frequencies which can penetrate the various regions at normal incidence. The maximum electron concentration is related to the critical frequency by the expression

$$N_m = 1.24 \times 10^4 \, f^2 \text{ electrons/cm}^3, \qquad (2\text{-}1)$$

where f is expressed in megacycles per second. In plasma physics, the critical frequency is known as the plasma frequency, but critical frequency is the term usually used in ionospheric work.

2.2. THE D REGION

The D region is the lowest ionospheric region. The altitude usually ascribed to it is from 60 to approximately 85 km. It is thought that the ionizing agent is hydrogen Lyman-alpha radiation and that the primary ions formed are NO$^+$ (Nicolet, 1945; Bates, 1956), although no measurements of the ionic constituents have been made. Lyman-alpha radiation cannot ionize the principal atmospheric constituents, but it can ionize nitric oxide, which is a minor constituent of the atmosphere. Nitric oxide has been detected spectroscopically (Barth, 1964), and its concentration appears to be greater than the amount thought to be required to explain the formation of the D region. Cosmic radiation also gives rise to some atmospheric ionization, and it makes a significant contribution to the lower portion of the normal D region (Nicolet and Aikin, 1960). Measurements of D-region electron concentrations are very difficult to make with ground-based techniques; however, rocket flights have provided some unambiguous data on the electron concentrations (Seddon and Jackson, 1958; Ichimiya et al., 1961; Adey and Heikkila, 1961; Barrington et al., 1963). The maximum electron concentration occurs near 80 km and is of the order of 10^3 electrons/cm^3. The electrons largely disappear at night, though the actual physical process involved is not well understood. Either recombination with positive ions or attachment to neutral particles to form negative ions may occur.

Because of the relatively high gas densities in the D region, electron collision frequencies there are high, and the region acts as a strong absorber of electro-magnetic energy. At night, when the electron concentration is negligible, the attenuation of communication signals is much less than in the daytime. Three separate types of electromagnetic-absorption phenomena are associated with certain solar flares (Reid and Collins, 1959). The first of these is called the sudden ionospheric disturbance (SID). These events last for half an hour or so and are associated with increased ionization in the lower D region, which in turn gives rise to strong attenuation of radio signals, resulting in radio black-outs. The increased ionization occurs during the daytime and is caused by X-rays emitted by the sun (Friedman et al., 1958a, 1958b). The second type of absorp-tion is closely associated with active auroras and magnetic disturbances. The absorption apparently takes place near the top of the D region and is predomi-nantly a nighttime effect. At high latitude, i.e., above the auroral zone, a third type of absorption takes place. These latter phenomena, called polar-cap black-outs, are caused by the penetration of energetic particles into the D region and below, following those flares which emit low-energy cosmic radiation (Bailey, 1959). The above absorption effects have sometimes been referred to as type I, type II, and type III absorptions, respectively. There is a strong positive cor-relation between all these effects and the 11-year sunspot cycle.

2.3. THE E REGION

The altitude range from approximately 85 to 140 km is designated the E region. It is now generally accepted that soft solar X-rays are mainly responsible for the photo-ionization which occurs in this altitude range (Bates, 1956; Fried-man, 1959). The main ionic species, as shown by rocket-borne mass spectrom-eters (Johnson et al., 1958; Istomin, 1960), are the diatomic ions O_2^+ and NO^+. NO^+ is the predominant ion except near 100 km during the daytime, when the two ion concentrations become comparable. With this exception, the concentra-tion of NO^+ exceeds that of O_2^+ by at least a factor of 3. The primary ions that are formed are N_2^+, O_2^+, and O^+. The N_2^+ ions dissociatively recombine very rapidly (Bates, 1951; Biondi, 1964), and they may also react chemically with oxygen, with the result that the concentration of N_2^+ is small. It was first recog-nized by Bates (1955) that ion-atom interchange reactions of the type

$$X^+ + YZ = XY^+ + Z \qquad (2\text{-}2)$$

should proceed rapidly in the ionosphere. Such chemical reactions of O^+ with O_2 and N_2 quickly remove the O^+ ions and produce either NO^+ or O_2^+ ions in their place.

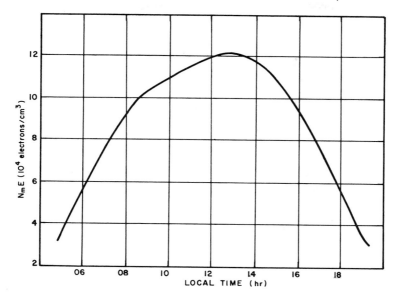

Fig. 2-2. Summer diurnal variation of N_mE (maximum electron concentration in the E region) at Slough. *Appleton (1959), reproduced with permission of Institute of Radio Engineers.*

The electron concentration in the E region is of the order of 10^5 electrons/cm^3 at noon during sunspot minimum and approximately 50 per cent larger during sunspot maximum. The electron concentration is highest near local noon and falls off symmetrically with time on either side of noon, as shown in **Fig. 2-2**, where the summer diurnal variation of the maximum electron concentration in the E region at Slough, England, has been plotted (Appleton, 1959).

The variation of the noon values of the maximum electron concentration in the E region with time of the year at Washington, D.C., and Slough are plotted in **Fig. 2-3** (Appleton, 1959). The electron concentrations are roughly twice as large in summer as in winter at Slough, while the variation at Washington is not quite as large.

A rather common perturbation of the electron concentration in the E region occurs near 100 km and consists of a thin layer (only a few kilometers thick) in which the electron concentration may be as much as twice as high as the ambient concentration just above and below the layer (Seddon and Jackson, 1958). The layer is called Sporadic E. Another possible mechanism to account for the phenomenon of Sporadic E, which is evidenced by anomalous reflection characteristics, may be the existence of steep gradients in the electron concentrations. It has recently been shown that equatorial Sporadic E is associated with the equatorial electrojet (Cohen and Bowles, 1963). The anomalous reflection in this

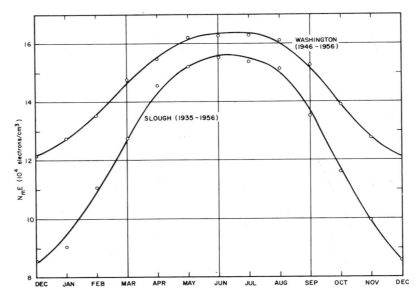

Fig. 2-3. Seasonal variations of monthly means of noon N_mE for Washington and Slough. Values were averaged over one sunspot cycle for Washington and over two for Slough. *Appleton (1959), reproduced with permission of Institute of Radio Engineers.*

case occurs from plane waves of electron concentration which are generated by a two-stream plasma instability taking place in the electrojet current system (Farley, 1963). The temporal variations of Sporadic E are complicated and have been summarized in detail on a worldwide basis by Smith (1957). Sporadic E usually occurs at night at high latitudes and in the daytime near the magnetic equator. Throughout the temperate latitudes, the main variation is a seasonal one, with much more Sporadic E occurring during summer than winter.

2.4. THE F_1 REGION

The altitude demarcations between the E and F_1 regions and the F_1 and F_2 regions are not cleanly defined, and we shall arbitrarily call the altitude range from 140 to 200 km the F_1 region. The solar spectrum in the wavelength band from 200 A to 900 A is principally responsible for the photo-ionization in this region, where several hundred electrons/cm³-sec are liberated (Hinteregger *et al.*, 1960). Because the photoelectrons are released with relatively high energy, which they share principally with other electrons, the electron temperature is several hundred degrees higher than the atmospheric temperature during the daytime (Hanson and Johnson, 1961 ; Spencer *et al.*, 1962). The predominant ions are NO^+ and O_2^+ near the low altitude boundary, and a gradual transition takes place until, at the upper boundary, O^+ is the principal ion (Johnson *et al.*, 1958). This is significant because of the greatly different recombination coefficients of the diatomic and monatomic ions, i.e., about 10^{-7} cm^3/sec and 10^{-12} cm^3/sec, respectively. The electron concentration is typically of the order of 2.5×10^5 electrons/cm^3 at noon during sunspot minimum and 4×10^5 electrons/cm^3 at noon during sunspot maximum. Large diurnal variations also occur in the F_1 region; the layer is not present at night, as a depression in electron concentration, or valley, develops above the E region. The valley is difficult to recognize on ionosonde records, but it has been explored with detectors flown in rockets (Ichimiya *et al.*, 1961).

2.5. THE F_2 REGION

Although $h_m F_2$, the altitude of the peak electron concentration in the F_2 region, changes considerably during the sunspot cycle, with latitude, and diurnally, we shall define the F_2 region as that lying in the altitude range from 200 to about 1,000 or 2,000 km, the lower limit being determined by the distribution of electron concentration and the upper limit by the change in ion composition in the transition region, which will be described in Section 2.6. The F_2 ionospheric region is probably the most difficult one to describe because of the many anomalies in its behavior (Martyn, 1959). The principal solar radiation responsible for the F_2-region ionization is probably the same as that for the F_1 region. The reason a second ionization peak is formed is that the recombination rate falls off more rapidly with altitude than does the ionization rate, so that larger ion concentrations occur at higher altitudes. Ultimately, downward diffusion of ions becomes faster than either ionization or recombination and causes the ion concentrations to decrease with altitude.

Mass-spectrometer measurements in satellites (Istomin, 1960; Poloskov, 1960) have shown that the principal ions present are O^+ and N^+, with O^+ greatly predominant. Most of the monatomic ions do not recombine directly with electrons but react chemically with O_2 and N_2 to form O_2^+ and NO^+ ions, which then recombine relatively rapidly, as do the primary diatomic ions which are formed by photo-ionization. Thus the limiting processes for recombination are chemical ones, since the time for an O^+ ion to react with a neutral molecule is much longer than the recombination lifetime of the diatomic ion formed in the process. Since the concentration of neutral molecules falls off rapidly with altitude, so does the effective recombination coefficient change rapidly with altitude (Havens *et al.*, 1955), as it is of the order of 10^{-9} cm^3/sec at the base of the F_2 region, 10^{-10} cm^3/sec at $h_m F_2$ (the altitude of maximum electron density), and 10^{-12} cm^3/sec at some level well above $h_m F_2$.

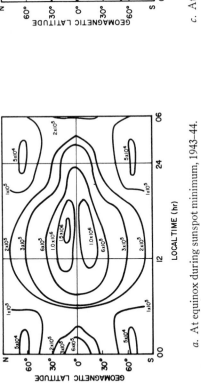

c. At summer solstice during sunspot minimum, 1943–44.

a. At equinox during sunspot minimum, 1943–44.

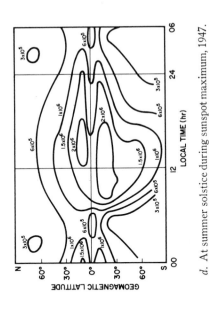

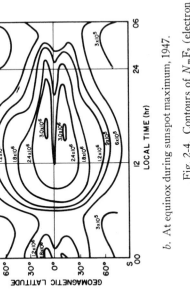

d. At summer solstice during sunspot maximum, 1947.

b. At equinox during sunspot maximum, 1947.

Fig. 2-4. Contours of $N_m F_2$ (electron concentrations at the F_2 peak) in electrons/cm³.

The electron concentration at the F_2 peak varies in a complicated manner (Martyn, 1959); this behavior is shown in **Fig. 2-4**. Data for times near the equinoxes and near sunspot-cycle minimum and maximum are shown in **Fig. 2-4a** and **2-4b**. It can be seen that there is a high degree of symmetry between the two hemispheres, but that there is a peculiar relative minimum in the electron concentration during the afternoon over the geomagnetic equator. Data for times near the summer solstice and near sunspot-cycle minimum and maximum are shown in **Fig. 2-4c** and **2-4d**. The relative minimum in electron concentration over the geomagnetic equator is still clear, but the symmetry at high latitudes is disturbed by the tilt of the north polar region toward the sun.

The behavior of h_mF_2, the height of the maximum electron concentration, is extremely complicated; some of its variations are shown in **Fig. 2-5** and **2-6**

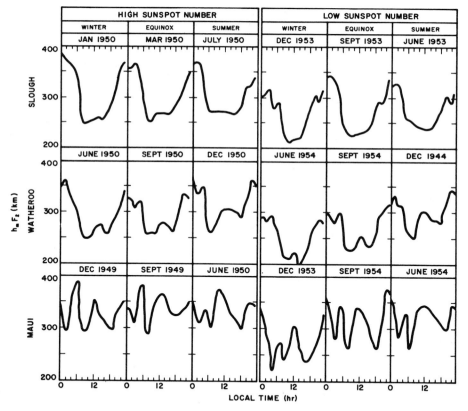

Fig. 2-5. Average variations of h_mF_2 (height of the F_2 peak) for 10 international quiet days in each month for three seasons in years of high and low sunspot number at three widely separated stations. *Thomas (1959), reproduced with permission of Institute of Radio Engineers.*

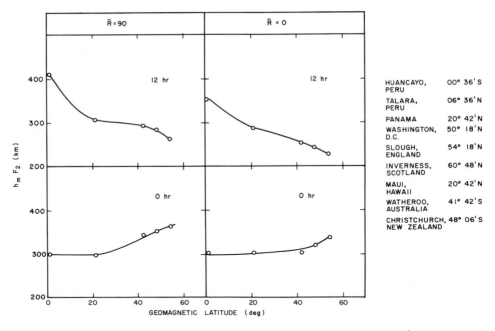

HUANCAYO, PERU	00° 36'S
TALARA, PERU	06° 36'N
PANAMA	20° 42'N
WASHINGTON, D.C.	50° 18'N
SLOUGH, ENGLAND	54° 18'N
INVERNESS, SCOTLAND	60° 48'N
MAUI, HAWAII	20° 42'N
WATHEROO, AUSTRALIA	41° 42'S
CHRISTCHURCH, NEW ZEALAND	48° 06'S

a. Averaged for an equinox month at two epochs of the sunspot cycle.

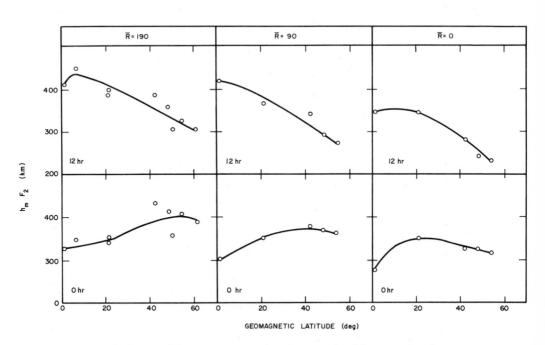

b. Averaged for a summer month at three epochs of the sunspot cycle.

Fig. 2-6. Variations of h_mF_2 with geomagnetic latitude.

(Thomas, 1959). **Figure 2-5** shows the change in $h_m F_2$ at three different stations as a function of local time at different times of the year and at high and low sunspot number; these data are for international quiet days (i.e., days when the ionosphere is relatively undisturbed and in reasonable agreement with the models shown in **Fig. 2-1**). The height of the maximum electron concentration varies from 200 to 400 km at these medium-latitude stations. **Figure 2-6a** shows the latitude dependence of $h_m F_2$ averaged at noon and midnight over an equinox month at two epochs of the solar cycle. The average sunspot number, $\overline{R}$, is near zero at the minima of the solar cycles and usually between 50 and 200 at the maxima, the average being about 100. **Figure 2-6b** shows the same quantities during summer at noon and midnight at three epochs of the solar cycle. Generally speaking, at high latitudes $h_m F_2$ is higher at night than during the day while near the equator the opposite is true. Also, there is a general trend for $h_m F_2$ to increase with solar activity.

Sometimes the F region shows a diffuse character which is attributed to clouds of electrons having concentrations different from the ambient surroundings. This condition is called "spread F," and it occurs mainly at night (Wright *et al.*, 1956). Since the dielectric constant of the ionosphere varies with the electron concentration, these inhomogeneities cause scintillation of signals from radio stars or other radio sources beyond the ionosphere. The phenomena of spread F occur more often at high latitudes during periods of high sunspot activity, show a minimum at all times near 35-deg geomagnetic latitude, and occur more often at low latitudes during periods of low sunspot activity.

2.6. THE OUTER IONOSPHERE

Because of the relatively small scale height of oxygen ions, their abundance quickly diminishes with increasing altitude above the F_2 peak, at a rate that depends very sensitively on temperature. For example, the oxygen ion concentration at 4000 km would be about 1 ion/cm³ for $T = 1600\,°K$, but only 10^{-4} ion/cm³ for $T = 800\,°K$. Hence, it was very surprising when Storey (1953) showed that the electron concentration was of the order of 10^3 electrons/cm³ at altitudes of several Earth radii, and it was at first assumed that this result was descriptive of interplanetary conditions rather than of the outer ionosphere. Storey deduced the electron concentration from his measurements and interpretation of the dispersion of radio whistlers. These low-frequency (1 to 30 kc/s) signals are generated by lightning strokes, and they follow paths along the Earth's magnetic field lines from one hemisphere to the other. They propagate out to very large distances from the Earth (occasionally as far as 8 Earth radii), and at present the main experimental evidence about the electron concentrations at great heights is provided by the dispersion of these waves.

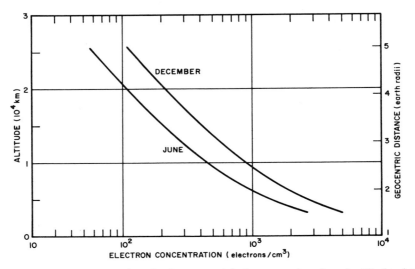

Fig. 2-7. Electron concentrations in the equatorial plane as a function of altitude, determined from nose-whistler data.

Fig. 2.7 shows a summary of ion concentrations in the Earth's magnetic equatorial plane (Smith, 1960) ; the two curves indicate an annual variation, the source of which is not understood. The data apply only in the equatorial plane, since it is the concentration in that region to which the whistler dispersion is mainly sensitive.

In order to have such large ion concentrations at great heights, it is necessary that the ionization present be characterized by a scale height of the order of 10^3 km near the base of the exosphere. Since unacceptably high temperatures would be needed to satisfy this requirement for oxygen ions, it is more reasonable to assume that the ions are protons. This upper region of the ionosphere, in which protons are believed to be the dominant ion, is often referred to as the protonosphere. The source of the ions in the protonosphere is due only in a minor degree to direct photo-ionization of atomic hydrogen ; most of the ionization arises through charge exchange in the upper portion of the F region (Dungey, 1955 ; Johnson, 1960) according to the reaction

$$O^+ + H \rightleftarrows H^+ + O . \tag{2-3}$$

In view of this source of ionization and the fact that the magnetic field links the protonosphere to the ionosphere rather than to interplanetary space, it is appropriate to regard the protonosphere as merely the outermost extension of the ionosphere.

Nicolet (1961) recognized from satellite drag measurements that helium gas forms an appreciable portion of the neutral atmosphere near 1000-km altitude. He also suggested that helium ions should play an important role in the upper ionosphere. This prediction has since been verified by several different experiments (Hanson, 1962; Taylor *et al.*, 1963).

The ion concentrations in regions of space other than the geomagnetic equatorial plane can be deduced from the whistler data if the ion mass and the ion and electron temperatures are known. The distribution can be calculated only along the magnetic field lines, using the modified barometric law (Johnson, 1960),

$$N(R) = A \exp \left[g_0 m R_0{}^2 / Rk \ (T_e + T_i) \right]$$
$$\exp \left[m\Omega^2 R^2 \cos^2 \theta / 2k \ (T_e + T_i) \right], \qquad (2\text{-}4)$$

where $N(R)$ is the ion concentration at geocentric distance R, A is a normalization constant, g_0 is the acceleration of gravity at geocentric distance R_0, m is the average ion mass, k is the Boltzmann constant, Ω is the angular rate of rotation of the earth on its axis, θ is the latitude, and T_e and T_i are respectively the electron and ion temperatures. **Fig. 2-8** shows the ion distributions along several magnetic field lines calculated according to Eq. 2-4, assuming that $T_e = T_i = 1250\,°\text{K}$ and that the ions are all hydrogen. The calculated distributions are normalized to agree with the whistler results in the geomagnetic equatorial

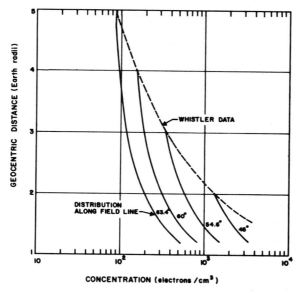

Fig. 2-8. The distribution of protons (or electrons) in the protonosphere at 4 latitudes. The dashed curve represents the concentrations in the equatorial plane determined from whistler experiments.

plane. If the temperatures are increased, the distributions become less dependent upon geocentric distance; if the temperatures were high enough so that the gravitational energy could be neglected by comparison with the average kinetic energy, the ions would be essentially trapped in the magnetic field and the concentration along a magnetic field line would show no dependence at all upon geocentric distance in the physical situation most likely to be encountered (i.e., isotropic velocity distribution).

Figure 2-8 indicates a marked variation with latitude in the ion and electron concentration in the lower protonosphere. This variation must result from the coupling between the protonosphere and the ionosphere in the transition region where they merge. In this region, the ionosphere consists of a multicomponent plasma; the three ions mentioned above, O^+, He^+, and H^+, are probably the more important ones, but a few per cent of atomic nitrogen ions are also present. It has also been suggested that O^{++} should be present (Nakada and Singer, 1962), but to date no ion mass-spectrometer data in this charge-to-mass range have been reported.

2.6.1. Diffusive Equilibrium Distribution

If there were no net fluxes of ions relative to one another in the outer ionosphere, the various ions would be distributed with altitude according to a diffusive equilibrium law. The distribution of a given ionic constituent with altitude can be stated rather simply when diffusive equilibrium prevails and when the temperatures of the ions, T_i, and of the electrons, T_e, do not vary with altitude z. The distribution of singly charged ions is given by

$$n_k(z) = v_k(z) \left\{ \sum_j n_{j0} / \sum_j v_j(z) \right\}^{T_e/(T_e + T_i)} \tag{2-5}$$

where n_{j0} is the concentration of the jth ion at a reference level z_0 and $v_j(z)$ represents the distribution the jth ion would have if its charge could be ignored; i.e.,

$$v_j(z) = n_{j0} \exp \left\{ - \int_{z_0}^{z} \frac{m_j g(z)}{kT_i} \, dz \right\}. \tag{2-6}$$

An additional term taking into account centrifugal forces should be included in (2-6) since the ionosphere rotates with the Earth. This centrifugal force term (which is represented in Eq. (2-4) by the second exponential) does not significantly affect the distribution of ions out to 3 or 4 Earth radii, beyond which almost nothing is known of the properties of the medium.

It follows immediately from (2-5) that the electron concentration is given by

$$n_e = \sum_k n_k = (n_{e0})^{T_e/(T_i + T_e)} \left\{ \sum_k v_k(z) \right\}^{T_i/(T_e + T_i)}. \tag{2-7}$$

It can also be shown that the altitude h_{kj} above z_0 at which two ions have the same concentration is given by

$$h_{kj} = \mathcal{H}_{kj} \left(1 - \frac{\mathcal{H}_{kj}}{R} \right)^{-1} , \qquad (2\text{-}8)$$

where R is the geocentric distance to the reference level z_0 and

$$\mathcal{H}_{kj} = \frac{\mathcal{H}_k \mathcal{H}_j}{\mathcal{H}_k - \mathcal{H}_j} \, ln \left(\frac{n_{j0}}{n_{k0}} \right) , \qquad (2\text{-}9)$$

where $\mathcal{H}_k = kT_i/m_k g_0$ and g_0 is the value of g at R. $\mathcal{H}_{kj}$ is the altitude above z_0 where the concentrations would be equal if g were constant and the charges on the ions could be ignored. For h_{kj} to be positive, m_j must be greater than m_k and n_{j0} must be greater than n_{k0}.

Any ion which has a negative scale height at the reference level (true for any ion that is lighter than the average ion mass) will have a maximum concentration above this level. This maximum occurs where

$$m_j = \left(\frac{T_i}{T_i + T_e} \right) \overline{m}_+ ; \qquad (2\text{-}10)$$

$\overline{m}_+$ is the average ion mass and it is given by

$$\overline{m}_+ = \sum_k m_k \, v_k(z) / \sum_k v_k(z) . \qquad (2\text{-}11)$$

2.6.2. The Transition Region

The transition region between the upper portion of the F region, where the predominant ion is O^+, and the protonosphere can be described in terms of the diffusive equilibrium ion distributions discussed in the previous section; however, such a description is an oversimplification and not a very good approximation to the actual situation, as will be shown below. **Fig. 2-9** shows a diffusive-equilibrium distribution; for the parameters chosen, O^+ is the predominant ion up to an altitude of 900 km, He^+ predominates from 900 to 1900 km, and H^+ predominates at higher altitudes. The region where helium ions predominate has been observed to be as much as 2000 km thick (Hanson, 1962), and at another stage in the sunspot cycle the region was nonexistent (Taylor *et al.*, 1963).

The hypothesis of diffusive equilibrium used in obtaining **Fig. 2-9** requires that there be no significant diffusive flow of ions. A calculation in which the diffusive flow of ions is taken into account would be more realistic. Helium ions are formed by photo-ionization at relatively high altitudes, and in general the ions must flow downward in order to recombine in processes which involve molecular species. Further, hydrogen ions can be expected to flow from the ionosphere into the protonosphere and back again, on a diurnal basis. Such

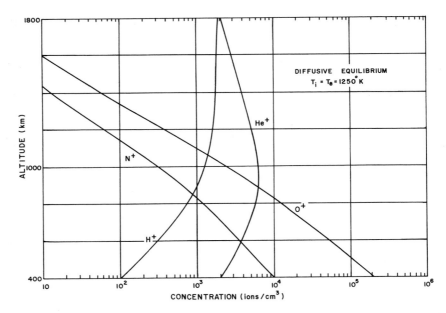

Fig. 2-9. The diffusive-equilibrium distribution of the principal ion constituents of the upper F region for $T_i = T_e = 1250$ °K. The relative concentrations at any particular level are arbitrary but reasonably typical of values encountered in the ionosphere under these temperature conditions.

flows will disturb the diffusive-equilibrium distributions. An example of this is shown in **Fig. 2-10**, which gives the results of mass-spectrometer measurements in the transition region made by Taylor *et al.* (1963); the dissimilarity in **Figs. 2-9** and **2-10** between the hydrogen and helium ion distributions in the region where they are minor ionic constituents is obvious. Hanson *et al.* (1963) have interpreted the hydrogen-ion distribution in **Fig. 2-10** as indicating an upward H+ ion flux of 1.3×10^7 ions/cm²-sec.

The transition region can be expected to be quite variable, depending upon the sunspot cycle and other disturbances. During magnetic storms, the protonosphere appears to become severely depleted at high latitudes (Carpenter, 1963); the depletion may occur rather rapidly, but the recovery time is probably several days. The scarcity of whistler data at high latitudes during magnetic storms tends to obscure the details of the recovery process. It has been suggested (Hanson, 1964) that heating of the protonosphere during a magnetic storm may allow the protons to be driven into the oxygen-ion region, because the coulomb-scattering cross section decreases rapidly with increasing particle energy. Once the protons are thermalized in the upper F region, they would diffuse back upward very slowly; this polarized penetration of the F region by protons is

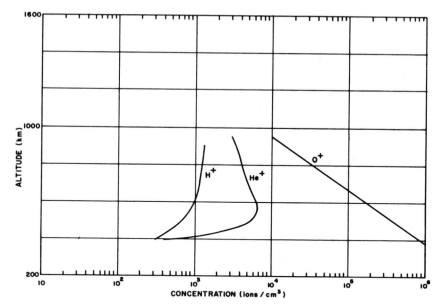

Fig. 2-10. Ion concentrations measured in the upper F region by Taylor *et al.* (1963). Comparison with Fig. 2-9 shows that the measured profiles do not resemble the diffusive-equilibrium profiles in the altitude region where the light ions are minor constituents.

akin to the solar radiation "greenhouse" effect. Using the flux 1.3×10^7 protons/cm²-sec obtained from **Fig. 2-10** and noting that the content of H⁺ ions in a magnetic flux tube above 1000 km is of the order of 10^{13} ions/cm², it can be seen that several days would be required to change the protonosphere content appreciably. Diurnal changes in the protonosphere must also be limited by the slowness with which ions can move upward from the F region; a small diurnal variation in protonosphere concentrations has been indicated by whistler measurements (Rivault and Corcuff, 1960).

The morphology of the helium ion layer is not well established, but it has been suggested that the total helium-ion content in a unit column should not have large diurnal changes (Hanson, 1962). Even this point has not been established. The projected use of light ion mass-spectrometers in several satellites should add greatly to our knowledge of the complicated behavior of the various ion species which play a role in the outer ionosphere.

2.6.3. Ionospheric Temperatures

It was first suggested by Hanson and Johnson (1961) that the daytime temperature of the ionospheric electrons in the lower F region is probably larger than the ambient gas temperature by a factor of the order of two. This situation arises because the ambient electrons are relatively efficient in removing the excess kinetic energy from the energetic photoelectrons which are continually released as a result of solar ultraviolet absorption by the atmosphere, and because there are relatively few electrons to share this energy. The hot electron gas is cooled primarily by collisions with neutral particles at altitudes below approximately 250 km and by collisions with ions at higher altitudes. The ions act as a heat transfer agent and pass on the heat they extract from the electrons to the neutral gas for conduction downward.

Measurements in rockets (Spencer *et al.*, 1962) have provided experimental evidence that the electron temperature is indeed higher than the gas temperature. The measurements also show that this temperature difference on occasion remains large even well above the F_2 peak. Bowles (1963) first demonstrated that the electron temperature was abnormally high in the morning. This fact is readily interpretable from the expression (Hanson and Johnson, 1961),

$$T_e - T = AQT_e^{3/2}/n_e^2 , \qquad (2\text{-}12)$$

where Q is the heat input to the electrons, and A is a constant ($A = 2.1 \times 10^6$ if Q is expressed in ev/cm³-sec). The heat input into the F-region electron gas builds up rapidly just after sunrise, since the optical depth is small. Since the electron concentration n_e is relatively small in the early morning hours, the number of electrons available to share the energy is small and the electron temperature increases drastically. This effect has been considered in detail by Dalgarno *et al.* (1963), who showed that the electron temperatures may become high enough to cause an appreciable excitation of atomic oxygen to the ¹D state (which is followed by emission of 6300 A radiation).

The fact that the electron temperatures during the daytime are considerably higher than the gas temperatures at altitudes above 300 km is probably due to the circumstance that photoelectrons released above 300 km have such a long mean free path that they can escape into the exosphere. Thus, they do not deposit their energy locally, but instead heat the electron gas in the outer ionosphere (Hanson, 1963). It is also possible that some electron heating occurs as a result of collisions with energetic trapped or precipitating particles.

With increasing altitude in the upper F region, the collisions between ions and neutral particles become very infrequent, and at sufficiently high altitudes the thermal coupling between electrons and ions predominates over that between the ions and neutral particles; above this altitude the ions tend to have the same temperature as the electrons. This crossover region has been estimated (Hanson, 1963) to be near 750 km, but it may occur 200 km higher or lower than this, depending on the ionospheric conditions.

A further effect which can cause a difference between the neutral-gas and charged-particle temperatures has been suggested by Megill and Carleton (1964). The presence of a strong electric field ($\sim$10mv/m) perpendicular to the Earth's magnetic field would cause the ionization to drift perpendicular to both the electric and magnetic fields at a velocity which is comparable to the thermal velocity of the ions. Collisions between the drifting ions and the neutral gas tend preferentially to heat up the ions (in the drift frame of reference) because their number density (or heat capacity per unit volume) is small compared with that of the neutral gas. Since the electrons are in good thermal contact with the ions above approximately 300 km, they too would become heated, but their temperature would be less than the ion temperature since they lose some of their energy in inelastic collisions with oxygen atoms (this latter effect becomes very important when T_e approaches 3000 °K). Megill et al. (1963) have suggested that this mechanism is responsible for the subauroral red arcs which are seen in the atomic oxygen 6300 A line near 400-km altitude (Marovich and Roach, 1963). A similar process takes place during the absorption of hydromagnetic waves (Dessler, 1959).

Satellite measurements (Brace et al., 1964) have shown that, for relatively low sunspot number, electron temperatures in the 300- to 800-km altitude range appear to be rather high ($\sim$2500 °K) in the early sunlit hours; they become somewhat lower during the day and then rise slightly in the afternoon. This behavior is in general accordance with Eq. (2-12). At night, T_e appears to be only a few hundred degrees higher than the gas temperature. The cause of the difference in the nighttime temperatures is not known. Near the equator, the electron and ion temperatures tend to approach equality at night, at least up to several thousand kilometers (K. Bowles, private communication).

2.7. IONOSPHERIC CONDUCTIVITIES AND COLLISION FREQUENCIES

The presence of electrons and ions in the ionosphere makes this atmospheric region electrically conducting. The concentrations of the charged particles and of the neutral particles govern the electrical conductivity, because collisions of charged particles restrict their movement under the action of any impressed electric field. The presence of a magnetic field greatly complicates the problem, as it restricts the motion of the charged particles across the magnetic field and therefore makes the conductivity anisotropic. Several different electrical conductivities must be defined for use in the different physical situations which occur.

Nicolet (1953) has given expressions for the collision frequencies of electrons with ions and with neutral particles. The collision frequency of electrons

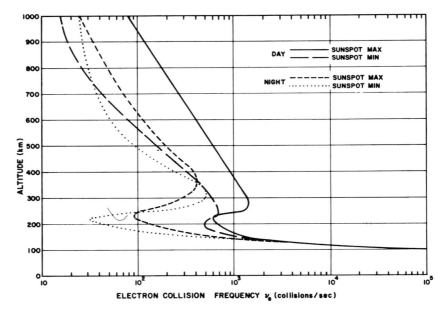

Fig. 2-11. Electron collision frequency ν_e versus altitude.

with neutral particles is given by the expression

$$\nu_{en} = 5.4 \times 10^{-10}\, n_n T_e^{1/2}\,, \tag{2-13}$$

where n_n is the concentration of neutral particles, and T_e is the electron temperature in degrees Kelvin. The expression

$$\nu_{ei} = [34 + 4.18 \log\,(T_e^3/n_e)]\, n_e T_e^{-3/2} \tag{2-14}$$

gives the collision frequency of electrons with ions. The electron-collision frequency with ions is much more temperature dependent than that with neutral particles, and in the opposite sense, because the collision cross section is highly dependent upon the velocity. The sum of the above two collision frequencies ν_{en} and ν_{ei} is plotted in **Fig. 2-11** as the electron collision frequency ν_e.

An expression for the frequency of collisions between ions and neutral particles was given by Chapman (1956) as

$$\nu_i = 2.6 \times 10^{-9}\, (n_n + n_i)\, M^{-1/2}\,, \tag{2-15}$$

where n_i is the ion concentration and M is the molecular weight of the ions and neutral particles, which are assumed to have the same mass. Equation 2-15 indicates that this collision frequency is not temperature-dependent; the collision frequency depends on the product of the velocity and the cross section, and thus it is velocity-independent (and therefore also temperature-independent) if the collision cross section varies inversely as the relative velocity. This is only approximately so, since Dalgarno (1958) has shown that the collision frequency of atomic oxygen ions with oxygen atoms is slightly temperature-dependent. One does not need to consider ion collisions with electrons; the electrons are so light that the ions essentially are not affected by encounters with electrons (although the electrons, of course, are greatly affected by their encounters with ions). The calculated collision frequencies for ions are shown in Fig. 2-12.

The specific electrical conductivity is that which exists parallel to a magnetic field or in the absence of a magnetic field, so it is often referred to as the zero-field conductivity. It is given by the expression

$$\sigma_0 = ne^2 \left[\frac{1}{m_e(v_e - i\omega)} + \frac{1}{m_i(v_i - i\omega)} \right], \qquad (2\text{-}16)$$

where e is the electronic charge (1.6×10^{-20} emu), n is the electron (or ion) concentration, m_e and m_i are the electron and ion masses, respectively, and ω is the impressed or driving frequency. Setting ω equal to zero and using data from Figs. 1-1, 1-2, and 2-1, the specific electrical conductivity was computed as a function of altitude. The result is shown in Fig. 2-13 for the extremes of

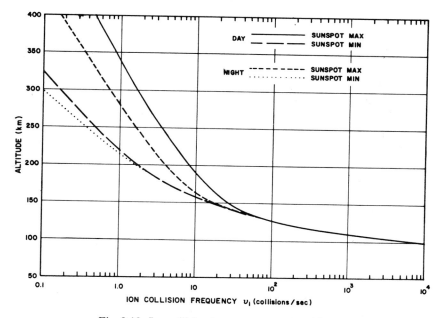

Fig. 2-12. Ion collision frequency v_i versus altitude.

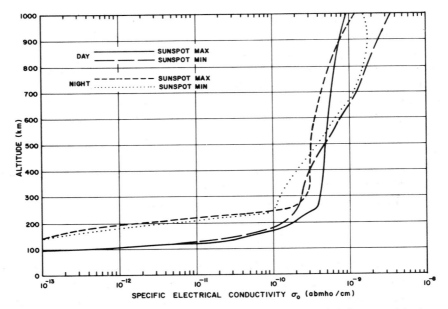

Fig. 2-13. Specific electrical conductivity σ_0 (zero-field conductivity) versus altitude.

the sunspot cycle and for daytime and nighttime. These data apply along the direction of the magnetic field if one is present or in problems where there is no magnetic field, provided the collision frequency is large compared with the impressed frequency.

The Pederson conductivity is that which applies perpendicular to the direction of the magnetic field **B** when one is present. It is sometimes referred to as the reduced conductivity because the presence of the magnetic field lowers the specific electrical conductivity (or zero-field conductivity) for problems involving the component of an electric field which is perpendicular to the magnetic field. The Pederson conductivity is given by the expression

$$\sigma_1 = n_e^2 \left\{ \frac{\nu_e - i\omega}{m_e[(\nu_e - i\omega)^2 + \omega_e^2]} + \frac{\nu_i - i\omega}{m_i[(\nu_i - i\omega)^2 + \omega_i^2]} \right\}, \quad (2\text{-}17)$$

where ω_e and ω_i are the electron and ion cyclotron frequencies, given respectively by Be/m_e and Be/m_i. The conductivities shown in **Fig. 2-14** were obtained with the same data as before. These conductivities are the ones to be used to compute the electric current in the direction of the component of an impressed electric field that is perpendicular to the magnetic field.

When an electric field **E** is applied in the presence of a magnetic field **B**, charged particles tend to drift in the direction **E** × **B**, which is perpendicular to the two fields. In the absence of collisions, the positive and negative particles

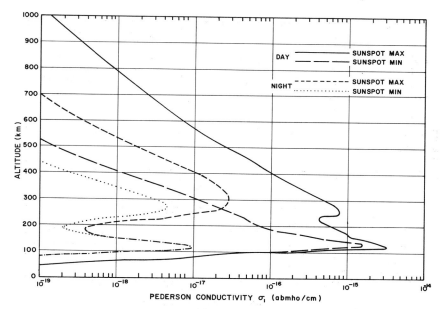

Fig. 2-14. Pederson conductivity σ_1 (reduced conductivity) versus altitude.

drift at the same speed and no current results. When collisions occur, the motions of the electrons and the ions are usually restricted in different degrees and a current results; this current is known as the Hall current. The conductivity used in computing this current is known as the Hall conductivity, which is given by the expression

$$\sigma_2 = n_e^2 \left\{ -\frac{\omega_e}{m_e[(\nu_e - i\omega)^2 + \omega_e^2]} + \frac{\omega_i}{m_i[(\nu_i - i\omega)^2 + \omega_i^2]} \right\}. \quad (2\text{-}18)$$

The conductivities shown in **Fig. 2-15** were obtained with the same data as before. These conductivities are to be used to compute the currents which flow in directions perpendicular to both the electric and magnetic field.

The Cowling conductivity, a combination of the Pederson and Hall conductivities, is useful in computing energy dissipation associated with currents in plasmas. The energy loss per unit volume due to a current flowing in a direction perpendicular to the magnetic field is given by j^2/σ_3, where j is the current density and σ_3 is the Cowling conductivity. In general, the current flow is not in the direction of the applied electrical field but has components due to both the Pederson conductivity σ_1 and the Hall conductivity σ_2. Since the energy dissipation per unit volume is given by either j^2/σ_3 *or* $j \cdot \mathbf{E}$, it follows that

$$\sigma_3 = \sigma_1 + \sigma_2^2/\sigma_1. \quad (2\text{-}19)$$

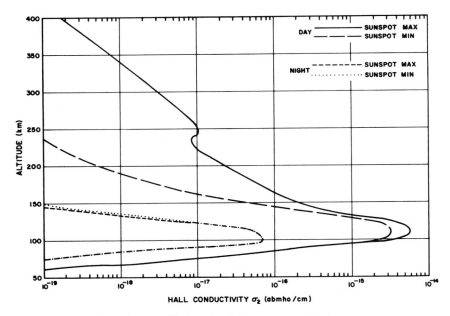

Fig. 2-15. Hall conductivity σ_2 versus altitude.

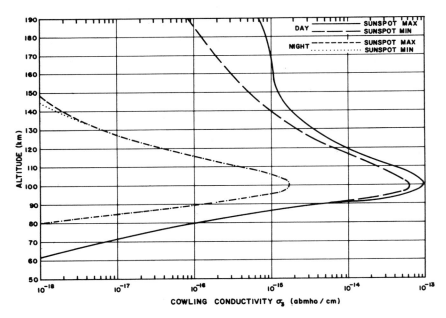

Fig. 2-16. Cowling conductivity σ_3 versus altitude.

The conductivities shown in **Fig. 2-16** were obtained with the previous data. Above 170 km, the Cowling conductivity is not significantly different from the Pederson conductivity.

The expressions given above for the various conductivities were taken from Francis and Karplus (1960). A complete treatment of the fundamental physics involved has been given by Chapman and Cowling (1939), and a lucid discussion of the entire ionospheric conductivity problem has been given by Chapman (1956).

The conductivities given in **Fig. 2-13** through **2-16** have been calculated for ω equal to zero, or for quasi-steady-state conditions, where the applied electric field does not change significantly in a time comparable to the various collision frequencies. However, Eq. (2-16) to (2-19) can be used to compute the conductivities when the impressed frequencies are comparable to, or greater than, the collision frequencies. A value of $B = 0.5$ gauss at sea level has been assumed in the evaluation of the cyclotron frequencies for the above calculations.

REFERENCES

Adey, A. W., and W. J. Heikkila. 1961. "Rocket Electron Density Measurements at Fort Churchill, Canada," *Canadian J. Physics;* **39**, 219–21.

Appleton, E. V. 1959. "The Normal E Region of the Ionosphere," *Proc. I.R.E.* **47**, 155–59.

Bailey, D. K. 1959. "Abnormal Ionization in the Lower Ionosphere Associated with Cosmic-Ray Flux Enhancements," *Proc. I.R.E.,* **47**, 255–56.

Barrington, R. E., E. V. Thrane, and B. Bjelland. 1963. "Diurnal and Seasonal Variations in D-Region Electron Densities Derived from Observations of Cross Modulation," *Canadian J. Physics,* **41**, 271–85.

Barth, C. A. 1964. "Rocket Measurement of the Nitric Oxide Dayglow," *Transactions American Geophysical Union,* **45**, 89.

Bates, D. R. 1951. "The Temperature of the Upper Atmosphere," *Proc. Phys. Soc. (London), B,* **64**, 805–21.

Bates, D. R. 1955. "Charge Transfer and Ion-Atom Interchange Collisions," *Proc. Phys. Soc. (London), A,* **68**, 344–45.

Bates, D. R. 1956. "Formation of the Ionized Layers," in W. J. G. Beynon and G. M. Brown, eds., *Solar Eclipses and the Ionosphere.* Pergamon Press, London, pp. 184–88.

Biondi, M. A. 1964. "Electron-Ion and Ion-Ion Recombination," *Ann. Geophys.,* **20**, 34–46.

Bowles, K. L., and staff. 1963. "Equatorial Electron Density Profiles to 5000 km, Using the Incoherent Scatter Technique," in W. Priester, ed., *Space Research III.* North-Holland Publishing Co., Amsterdam, pp. 253–64.

Brace, L. H., N. W. Spencer, and A. Dalgarno. 1964. "Electrostatic Probe Data and Interpretation," *Transactions American Geophysical Union,* **45**, 82.

Carpenter, D. L. 1963. "Whistler Evidence of a 'Knee' in the Magnetospheric Ionization Density Profile," *J. Geophys. Research,* **68**, 1675–82.

Chapman, S. 1956. "The Electrical Conductivity of the Ionosphere: a Review," *Nuovo cimento,* **4**, suppl., 1385–1412.

Chapman, S., and T. G. Cowling. 1939. *The Mathematical Theory of Non-Uniform Gases.* Cambridge University Press.

Cohen, R., and K. L. Bowles. 1963. "The Association of Plane-Wave Electron-Density Irregularities with the Equatorial Electrojet," *J. Geophys. Research,* **68,** 2503–25.

Dalgarno, A. 1958. "The Mobilities of Ions in Their Parent Gases," *Philosophical Transactions of the Royal Society (A),* **250,** 426–39.

Dalgarno, A., M. B. McElroy, and R. J. Moffett. 1963. "Electron Temperatures in the Ionosphere," *Planet. Space Sci.,* **11,** 463–84.

Dessler, A. J. 1959. "Upper Atmosphere Density Variations Due to Hydromagnetic Heating," *Nature,* **184,** 261–62.

Dungey, J. W. 1955. "The Electrodynamics of the Outer Exosphere," in *The Physics of the Ionosphere.* Physical Society, London, pp. 229–36.

Farley, D. T. 1963. "A Plasma Instability Resulting in Field-Aligned Irregularities in the Ionosphere," *J. Geophys. Research,* **68,** 6083–97.

Francis, W. E., and R. Karplus. 1960. "Hydromagnetic Waves in the Ionosphere," *J. Geophys. Research,* **65,** 3593–3600.

Friedman, H. 1959. "Rocket Observations of the Ionosphere," *Proc. I.R.E.,* **47,** 272–80.

Friedman, H., T. A. Chubb, J. E. Kupperian, and J. C. Lindsay. 1958a. "X-ray and Ultraviolet Emission of Solar Flares," *I.G.Y. Rocket Report Series 1,* IGY World Data Center A, National Academy of Sciences, Washington, pp. 179–82.

Friedman, H., T. A. Chubb, J. E. Kupperian, and J. C. Lindsay. 1958b. "X-ray Emission of Solar Flares," *I.G.Y. Rocket Report Series 1,* IGY World Data Center A, National Academy of Sciences, Washington, pp. 183–85.

Hanson, W. B. 1962. "Upper Atmosphere Helium Ions," *J. Geophys. Research,* **67,** 183–88.

Hanson, W. B. 1963. "Electron Temperatures in the Upper Atmosphere," in W. Priester, ed., *Space Research III.* North-Holland Publishing Co., Amsterdam, pp. 282–302.

Hanson, W. B. 1964. "Dynamic Diffusion Processes in the Exosphere," in E. Thrane, ed., *Electron Density Distribution in Ionosphere and Exosphere.* North-Holland Publishing Co., Amsterdam, pp. 361–70.

Hanson, W. B., and F. S. Johnson. 1961. "Electron Temperatures in the Ionosphere," *Mémoires, Soc. Roy. Sci., Liége,* **4,** 390–424.

Hanson, W. B., T. N. L. Patterson, and S. S. Degaonkar. 1963. "Some Deductions from a Measurement of the Hydrogen Ion Distribution in the High Atmosphere, *J. Geophys. Research,* **68,** 6203–5.

Havens, R. J., H. Friedman, and E. O. Hulburt. 1955. "The Ionospheric F₂ Region," in *The Physics of the Ionosphere.* The Physical Society, London, pp. 237–44.

Hinteregger, H. E., K. R. Damon, L. Heroux, and L. A. Hall. 1960. "Telemetering Monochromator Measurements of Solar 304 A Radiation and Its Attenuation in the Upper Atmosphere," in H. Kallmann Bijl, ed., *Space Research.* North-Holland Publishing Co., Amsterdam, pp. 615–27.

Ichimiya, T. E., K. Takayama, T. Dote, Y. Aona, K. Hirao, S. Miyazaki, T. Sugiyama, and T. Muraoka. 1961. "Measurement of Positive-Ion Density in the Ionosphere by Sounding Rocket," *Nature,* **190,** 156–58.

Istomin, V. G. 1960. "An Investigation of the Ionic Composition of the Earth's Atmosphere Using Rockets and Satellites," in L. V. Kurnosova, ed., *Artificial Earth Satellites,* Vol. 2. Plenum Press, New York, pp. 40–44.

Johnson, C. Y., E. B. Meadows, and J. C. Holmes. 1958. "Ion Composition of the Arctic Ionosphere," *J. Geophys. Research,* **63,** 443–44.

Johnson, F. S. 1960. "The Ion Distribution above the F₂ Maximum," *J. Geophys. Research,* **65,** 577–84.

Marovich, E., and F. E. Roach. 1963. "Distribution of Latitude of Red Arcs," *J. Geophys. Research,* **68,** 1885–88.

Martyn, D. F. 1959. "The Normal F Region of the Ionosphere," *Proc. I. R. E.,* **47,** 147–55.

Megill, L. R., and N. P. Carleton. 1964. "Excitation by Local Electric Fields in the Aurora and Airglow," *J. Geophys. Research,* **69**, 101–22.

Megill, L. R., M. H. Reis, and L. K. Droppleman. 1963. "Electric Fields in the Ionosphere and the Excitation of the Red Lines of Atomic Oxygen," *Planet. Space Sci.* **11**, 45–56.

Nakada, M. P., and S. F. Singer. 1962. "Multiply Ionized Oxygen in the Magnetosphere." URSI Spring Meeting, Washington, D.C.

Nicolet, M. 1945. "Contribution à l'étude de la structure de l'ionosphère," *Inst. Roy. Météor., Belgique, Mémoires,* **19**, 124.

Nicolet, M. 1953. "The Collision Frequency of Electrons in the Ionosphere," *J. Atmos. Terrest. Phys.,* **3**, 200–211.

Nicolet, M. 1961. "Helium, an Important Constituent in the Lower Exosphere," *J. Geophys. Research,* **66**, 2263–64.

Nicolet, M., and A. C. Aikin. 1960. "The Formation of the D Region of the Ionosphere," *J. Geophys. Research,* **65**, 1469–83.

Poloskov, S. M. 1960. "Upper Atmosphere Structure Parameters According to Data Obtained from U.S.S.R. Rockets and Satellites during IGY," in H. Kallmann Bijl, *Space Research.* North-Holland Publishing Co., Amsterdam, pp. 95–116.

Reid, G. C., and C. Collins. 1959. "Observations of Abnormal VHF Radio Wave Absorption at Medium and High Latitudes," *J. Atmos. Terrest. Phy.,* **14**, 63–81.

Rivault, R., and Y. Corcuff. 1960. "Recherche du Point Conjuge Magnetique de Poitiers Variation Nocturne de la Dispersion des Sifflements," *Ann. Geophys.,* **16**, 550–54.

Seddon, J. C., and J. E. Jackson. 1958. "Ionospheric Electron Densities and Differential Absorption," *Ann. Geophys.,* **14**, 456–63.

Smith, E. K. 1957. "Worldwide Occurrence of Sporadic E," National Bureau of Standards Circular No. 582.

Smith, R. L. 1960. "The Use of Nose Whistlers in the Study of the Outer Ionosphere," Technical Report No. 6, Contract AF18(603)-126, Stanford Electronics Laboratories, Stanford, Calif.

Spencer, N. W., L. H. Brace, and G. R. Carignan. 1962. "Electron Temperature Evidence for Non-Thermal Equilibrium in the Ionosphere," *J. Geophys. Research,* **67**, 157–75.

Storey, L. R. O. 1953. "An Investigation of Whistling Atmospherics," *Phil. Trans. Roy. Soc. (London), A,* **246**, 113–41.

Taylor, H. A., Jr., L. H. Brace, H. C. Brinton, and C. R. Smith. 1963. "Direct Measurements of Helium and Hydrogen Ion Concentration and Total Ion Density to an Altitude of 940 Kilometers," *J. Geophys. Research,* **68**, 5339–47.

Thomas, J. O. 1959. "The Distribution of Electrons in the Ionosphere," *Proc. I.R.E.,* **47**, 162–75.

Wright, R. W., J. R. Koster, and N. J. Skinner. 1956. "Spread F Layer Echoes and Radio-Star Scintillation," *J. Atmos. Terrest. Phys.,* **8**, 240–46.

3. Penetrating Particle Radiation

A. J. Dessler and B. J. O'Brien

Department of Space Science,
Rice University, Houston, Texas

3. Penetrating Particle Radiation

A. J. Dessler and B. J. O'Brien

Department of Space Science,
Rice University, Houston, Texas

3.1. INTRODUCTION

The radiations described in this chapter are those particle radiations that can penetrate more than about a milligram per square centimeter of material. The range-energy relationship for various penetrating radiations is shown in **Fig. 3-1**. The surface of the Earth is protected from most of the penetrating radiation found in space by the atmosphere, which constitutes approximately 10^3 g/cm² of shielding. The geomagnetic field exerts a major influence on charged-particle radiation near the Earth. Therefore the intensity of radiation around the Earth will, in general, be altitude-dependent and latitude-dependent. The penetrating radiations that a rocket or satellite vehicle encounters are, with few exceptions, unobservable at the Earth's surface. Thus such vehicles are required to investigate the space radiation environment. For example, the existence of the Van Allen radiation belt—the most intense naturally occurring penetrating-radiation flux now known to be present in space—was not even suspected before it was discovered in 1958 by means of the Explorer 1 satellite system.

3.2. GEOMAGNETICALLY TRAPPED RADIATION

Geomagnetically trapped radiation may be subdivided into two principal types according to origin: (1) the Van Allen radiation—naturally occurring high-energy trapped particles (both protons and electrons, and possibly alpha particles), and (2) Starfish radiation—the code name of the artificial radiation consisting principally of relativistic electrons impulsively injected into the geomagnetic field by a high-altitude nuclear explosion in July 1962.

In order to understand the nature of geomagnetically trapped radiation, it is necessary first to understand the motion of an individual charged particle trapped in a dipole-like field; this motion is discussed in Section 3.2.1. In Section 3.2.2, (B, L) and (R, λ) magnetic coordinates are discussed. The Van Allen radiation belt is described in Sections 3.2.3 through 3.2.5, and the Starfish radiation in Section 3.2.6.

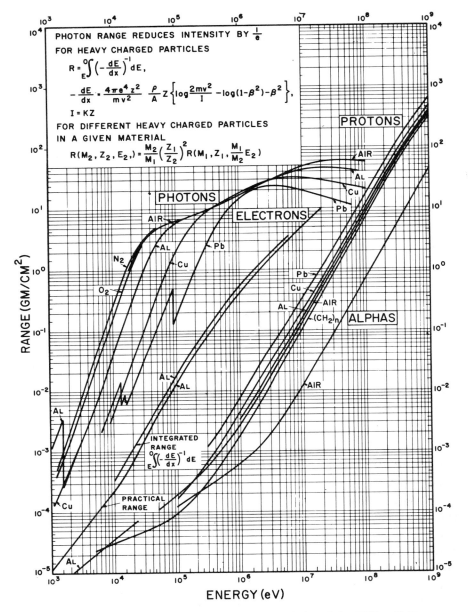

PHOTON RANGE REDUCES INTENSITY BY $\frac{1}{e}$

FOR HEAVY CHARGED PARTICLES

$$R = \int_E^0 \left(-\frac{dE}{dx}\right)^{-1} dE,$$

$$-\frac{dE}{dx} = \frac{4\pi e^4 z^2}{m v^2} \frac{\rho}{A} Z \left\{ \log \frac{2mv^2}{I} - \log(1-\beta^2) - \beta^2 \right\},$$

$$I = KZ$$

FOR DIFFERENT HEAVY CHARGED PARTICLES
IN A GIVEN MATERIAL

$$R(M_2, Z_2, E_2,) = \frac{M_2}{M_1} \left(\frac{Z_1}{Z_2}\right)^2 R\left(M_1, Z_1, \frac{M_1}{M_2} E_2\right)$$

PROTONS

PHOTONS

ELECTRONS

AIR
AL
Cu
Pb

N₂
O₂
AL
Cu
Pb

Pb
Cu
AL
(CH₂)ₙ
AIR

ALPHAS

AIR

AL
AL

AL

INTEGRATED
RANGE
$$\int_E^0 \left(-\frac{dE}{dx}\right)^{-1} dE$$

Cu

PRACTICAL
RANGE

AL

RANGE (GM/CM²)

ENERGY (eV)

Fig. 3-1. Range-energy curves for penetrating radiations (after Fillius, 1963).

3.2.1. Motion of a Charged Particle Trapped in the Geomagnetic Field

The Van Allen radiation belt is a band of energetic-particle radiation trapped in the geomagnetic field. Excellent discussions of the physics of particles trapped in a dipole field have been given by Alfvén and Fälthammar (1963) and by Northrop (1963). A brief description of the particle motion is given below, but the reader is referred to the books by Alfvén and Fälthammar and Northrop for detailed derivations and other pedagogical points.

A charged particle trapped in the geomagnetic field executes a complex motion. However, this complex motion can be divided into three simple components, which are described below.

1. A particle moves in a circle of radius $a = mv_\perp c/(ZeB)$ with an angular frequency $\omega_c = ZeB/(mc)$, where m is the mass of the particle, $v_\perp$ is its component of velocity perpendicular to the local magnetic field direction, c is the velocity of light, Ze is the particle charge in esu, and B is the magnitude of the local magnetic field in gauss. For Van Allen radiation particles, $a << r$, where r is the distance to the center of the Earth from the magnetic field line about which the particle is spiraling. This circular motion is properly called cyclotron motion; a is the cyclotron radius and ω_c is the cyclotron frequency. The center of the circle is called the particle's guiding center. The period of the cyclotron motion is designated T_1.

2. The guiding center of a particle whose velocity vector makes an angle α (the pitch angle) with the magnetic field direction at a position where the field strength is B moves almost parallel to the field line until it reaches a position where the field strength is $B_m = B/\sin^2\alpha$, where B_m is the maximum field strength to which the particle can penetrate. The position at which $B = B_m$ is called the mirror point, since a particle reaching this point will be reflected back along the field line. Thus the guiding center of a particle trapped in the geomagnetic field moves very nearly parallel to a field line (see 3 below) and bounces back and forth between northern- and southern-hemisphere mirror points A and A^* at latitudes λ_A and λ_{A^*} with a period T_2, given by

$$T_2 = 2 \int_{A^*}^{A} \frac{dl}{v_{||}} , \tag{3-1}$$

where the integral is taken along the magnetic field line or along the line of guiding center motion, and where $v_{||}$ is the velocity parallel to this line. By treatment of the motion of trapped particles (Hamlin *et al.*, 1961), this can be written as

$$T_2 = \frac{2}{v} \int_{A^*}^{A} \frac{dl}{\sqrt{1 - B/B_m}}, \tag{3-2}$$

where B_m is the magnetic field strength at A and A^*. A convenient expression for motion in the geomagnetic field is then

$$T_2 = 0.085 \frac{R_o}{\beta} T(\alpha_0) \text{ seconds},\tag{3-3}$$

where $T(\alpha_0) \approx 1.30 - 0.56 \sin \alpha_0$, α_0 is the equatorial pitch angle at a geocentric equatorial distance R_0, and $\beta = v/c$.

3. As a trapped particle bounces back and forth between mirror points, its guiding center slowly drifts in longitude with a period T_3; positively charged particles drift westward and negatively charged particles drift eastward. The particle's guiding center traces out a magnetic shell that in a perfect dipole field would lie on a surface defined by the figure of revolution of a magnetic field line. A magnetic field line in a dipole field is given by

$$r = R_o \cos^2 \lambda,\tag{3-4}$$

where r is the geocentric distance to a point on the magnetic field line, R_o is the geocentric distance at which the field line crosses the equatorial plane, and λ is the angle between the equator and the point on the magnetic field line (i.e., the geomagnetic latitude).

$$T_3 \approx 172.4 \; \frac{1 + \varepsilon}{\varepsilon(2 + \varepsilon)} \frac{1}{mR_0} \frac{G}{F} \text{ minutes},\tag{3-5}$$

where

$$\varepsilon = \left[\frac{1}{\sqrt{1 - \beta^2}} \right] - 1,$$

and G/F is a function of the mirroring latitude and is of order unity (Hamlin et al., 1961). The above description of the motion of a particle trapped in a magnetic field applies for an undistorted dipole. In a field that is slightly distorted, as is the Earth's field, the situation is somewhat more complicated, and invariants of the motion are required to describe the motion exactly.

Three invariants describe the motion of a charged particle trapped in a static magnetic field. Each of these invariants will be described briefly with respect to the Van Allen radiation belt. (For a more detailed discussion, with many references to previous work on this subject, see Northrop [1963]). The three invariants are as follows:

1. The first invariant is the adiabatic or magnetic-moment invariant. The magnetic moment of a charged particle in a magnetic field is given by $\mu = \frac{1}{2} mv_\perp^2/B$, where m is the mass of the particle, $v_\perp$ is its component of velocity perpendicular to the local magnetic field direction, and B is the magnitude of the local magnetic field. As long as the particle motion and field configuration

are such that the magnetic field strength changes only slightly or linearly over the distance the particle moves in one cyclotron period, the magnetic moment remains constant, i.e., $v_\perp^2/B$ is a constant of the motion. Therefore,

$$\frac{\sin^2 \alpha}{B} = \frac{1}{B_m} = \text{constant} .$$

2. The second invariant is the integral or longitudinal invariant. The integral invariant is given by $I = \int v_{||} \, dl$, where $v_{||}$ is the component of the particle velocity parallel to the local magnetic field, dl is the element of length along the line of force, and the integral is evaluated between mirror points. This invariant of the motion places an additional constraint on the motion of a trapped particle. If a trapped particle drifts in the geomagnetic field so that μ and I are constant, the particle must drift in such a way that it eventually returns to the same field line from which it started. The constancy of μ requires only that B_m be constant; the additional constancy of I requires that the particle drift along a well defined integral-invariant surface.

3. The third invariant is the flux invariant, which is simply the net magnetic flux inside the integral-invariant surface defined in 2. That is, the flux invariant Φ is given by

$$\Phi = \int_S \mathbf{B} \cdot d\mathbf{s} ,$$

where $d\mathbf{s}$ is an element of area. The integral is evaluated over any surface connected to the integral-invariant surface and passing once (or any odd number of times) through the Earth's dipole axis, as indicated in **Fig. 3-2**. The constancy of Φ requires that, if the geomagnetic field were slowly to contract or expand (as happens during some phases of geomagnetic storms), the integral-invariant surface must change its size accordingly, so that Φ is conserved. During this process, μ and I also remain constant. An alternative way of stating the flux invariant is that the guiding center of the drifting particle follows slow movements of the magnetic field.

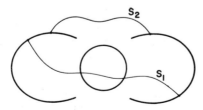

Fig. 3-2. The flux invariant is the magnetic flux passing through any surface connected to the integral-invariant shell and passing through the Earth's magnetic axis, as shown by the arbitrary surfaces S_1 or S_2.

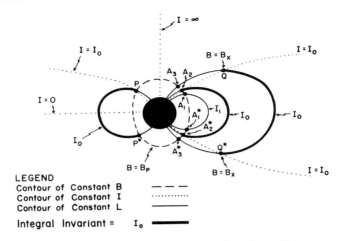

Fig. 3-3. Illustration of the application of the first two invariants. Suppose a particle initially mirrors at P and P^*, with $I = I_o$ and $B = B_P$. Then, when it drifts in longitude, it could mirror at $A_1A_1^*$ or $A_3A_3^*$, and satisfy the first invariant only, or it could mirror at QQ^* and satisfy the second invariant only. To satisfy both invariants it can mirror only at $A_2A_2^*$.

The applicability of these invariants can be seen by reference to **Fig. 3-3.** Suppose we have a trapped particle which mirrors at P and P^*. It therefore has $I = I_o$ and $B_m = B_{P'}$. We wish to know where it will be when it drifts in longitude, say to the right-hand side of the figure. It could mirror at Q and Q^* and satisfy I and I_o, but then $B_X \neq B_P$, so that the second but not the first invariant would be conserved. The situation is reversed if it mirrored at A_1 and A_1^*, or A_3 and A_3^*. Only if it mirrors at A_2 and A_2^* will both invariants be conserved, and hence that is where it will mirror.

One of the useful and instructive results of the integral-invariant calculation is shown in **Fig. 3-4,** in which the integral-invariant calculations of Jensen et al. (1960) are used to indicate some paths or traces that would be described by the mirror points of particles trapped in the geomagnetic field. Mirror-point altitudes are shown along the traces for particles that were arbitrarily selected to have mirror points at altitudes near 1500 km in the vicinity of 120° East longitude. The trace labeled $L = 1.17$ is the magnetic-invariant equator for this particular set of altitudes, i.e., the path of a drifting particle whose northern and southern mirror points are coincident, or whose pitch angle is 90 deg. (The significance of L is treated in Section 3.2.2.) The remaining traces are conjugate traces, i.e., the corresponding traces in the northern and southern (geomagnetic) hemispheres followed by mirror points of selected particles.

The three invariants can be violated or broken down by transient variations in the geomagnetic field, so that they are no longer constants of the particle's

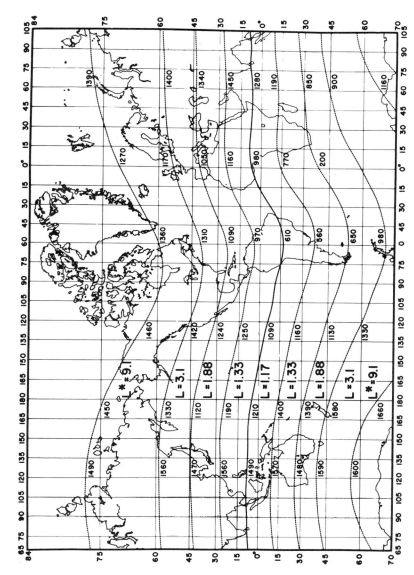

Fig. 3-4. Paths described by mirror points of particles trapped in the geomagnetic field, as indicated by the integral invariant. The mirror altitudes, arbitrarily chosen to be roughly 1500 km at 120° E longitude, are given at 60° intervals along each trace. The L value is given for each trace. The trace labeled $L = 1.17$ is the integral-invariant equator for this particular set. The other traces are conjugate pairs and are labeled with their respective L values. L and L^* are discussed in Section 3.2.2.

motion. This breakdown is caused by changes in the magnetic field in a time short compared with a characteristic motion. For example, the first (or magnetic moment) invariant can be broken down if the field changes in a time of the order of or less than the cyclotron period (Dragt, 1961; Dungey, 1963a; Cornwall, 1964). Similarly, the second (or integral) invariant can be broken down by changes in the field that occur in a time of the order of or less than the bounce period, i.e., the travel time between mirror points (Parker, 1961a); and the third (or flux) invariant by field changes in a time of the order of or less than the time required for a trapped particle to drift around the Earth (Parker, 1960). The third invariant can also be broken down by time-varying electric fields in the magnetosphere (Gold, 1959; Dungey, 1963b; Fejer, 1964).

It appears that, except in the inner zone of the Van Allen radiation belt, the third invariant is so easily violated that it is of limited value in deducing the long-term behavior of the Van Allen radiation. The first and second invariants, on the other hand, appear to be relatively stable.

All of the above discussion concerns trapped particles, viz., those that mirror above the sensible atmosphere (i.e., above 100 km). Those particles with pitch angles sufficiently small so that their mirror points are below $\sim$100 km are lost, i.e., precipitated. The loss cone is defined as an imaginary cone whose axis is along the magnetic field line and whose apex angle is equal to the pitch angle of a particle that will mirror at 100 km. Thus, particles "inside the loss cone" have pitch angles so small that they will mirror below 100 km and become precipitated rather than trapped particles.

3.2.2. The (R_o, λ) and the (B, L) Coordinate Systems

Within a geocentric distance R of about $6R_E$, the Earth's magnetic field is well represented by field sources within the Earth; i.e., deformation of the geomagnetic field by the solar wind is not important at these geocentric distances. (See Section 8.5 for a discussion of this point.) Thus, for $R < 6R_E$, it should be possible to devise coordinate systems for trapped radiation that are axially degenerate so that data taken at any point can be presented in a two-dimensional plot. Beyond $6R_E$ the solar wind will cause gross asymmetries.

The (R, λ) coordinate system, the first one to achieve wide use, is based on the centered dipole (see Section 8.3). R is the distance from the center of the Earth to the point of the measurement, and λ is the geomagnetic latitude (shown in **Fig. 8-8**). An improvement on this system could be obtained by using the eccentric dipole for the origin of the coordinates and using dip instead of geomagnetic latitude.

A more sophisticated form of the (R, λ) system is the (R_o, λ) system used by Fan *et al.* (1961). In this system, it is assumed that the dipole relationship, $R = R_o \cos^2 \lambda$, holds with good accuracy for the geomagnetic field. Then, data can be ordered in terms of the geomagnetic latitude and the equatorial crossing a distance of the field line on which the data were obtained. For example, if a measurement were made at $R = 2R_E$ and $\lambda = 45°$, the measurement would have the (R_o, λ) coordinates of $4R_E$ and $45°$ respectively. The (R, λ) and the (R_o, λ) coordinate systems do not work well near the Earth because of the higher-order, non-dipole components of the geomagnetic field and the displacement of the center of the main magnetic field relative to the geographic center. These systems are self-consistent within about 1 per cent of the geocentric distance between about 3 and $6R_E$. Closer to the Earth, the accuracy deteriorates until, at the Earth's surface, the error may be of the order of 10 per cent.

The (B, L) coordinate system proposed by McIlwain (1961) is in many ways similar to the (R_o, λ) system, but because it is based on the integral invariant calculated for the real geomagnetic field, it is accurate to about 1 per cent of the geocentric distance between 1 and 6 R_E. (Also see Stone (1963) for a detailed discussion and comparison of (R_o, λ) and (B, L) coordinate systems.)

The integral invariant (described in 3.2.1) enables one to determine the shell along which a trapped particle will drift in the complex geomagnetic field. In a pure dipole field, two particles that start out on the same integral-invariant surface will remain on that surface independent of their mirror fields B_m. However, in the Earth's field, the shape of an integral-invariant shell is a function of B_m. That is, two particles that start out on the same field line, but with different mirroring fields, will not remain together as they drift around the Earth, but will drift apart radially. The amount of radial splitting is approximately 1 per cent of the geocentric distance to the equatorial crossing of the integral-invariant shells. By ignoring this small radial splitting, McIlwain was able to order the motion of the trapped radiation by giving each point in space an L value that corresponds to the distance (in Earth radii) from the magnetic center of the Earth to the equatorial crossing of the field line that passes through that point. The field strength at that point is calculated by using a high-order spherical harmonic expansion. Each point in space is thus labeled by the magnetic field strength B and an equatorial crossing distance L.

Figure 3-5 shows the (R, λ) coordinate system on a (B, L) plane. Note that the (B, L) plot tends to enlarge the high-latitude regions and may make them seem relatively more significant.

Figure 3-6 shows the geographical distribution of L values over a surface arbitrarily chosen to be at 500-km altitude. From this figure it may be seen that significant errors can result if one attempts to transform the low-latitude L values into "integral-invariant latitudes" by using the relationship $R = L \cos^2 \lambda_I$.

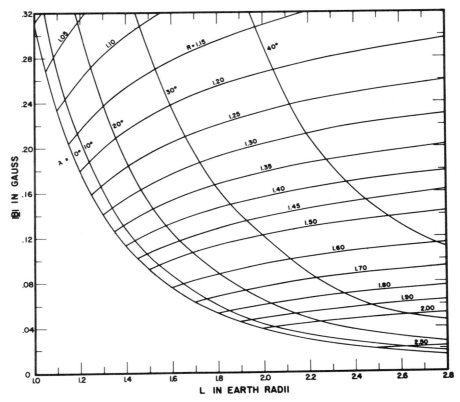

Fig. 3-5. The (R, λ) coordinate system mapped on to the (B, L) plane for a perfect dipole (after McIlwain, 1961).

For example, the figure portrays the surface $R = 1.08$ (corresponding to 500-km altitude), but the contours $L = 1$ and $L = 1.10$ do not bracket an equatorial contour $\lambda_I = 0°$. In order to obtain a contour of integral-invariant latitude, R must be varied continuously, as in **Fig. 3-4**.

In summary, the (B, L) coordinate system is particularly useful for accurate (~ 1 per cent) organization of data between geocentric distances of 1 to 3 R_E and below about 70° magnetic latitude. Two disadvantages of the (B, L) system are: (1) it requires a digital computer for most uses, and (2) the spatial configuration of data on a (B, L) plot is not simply related to its actual configuration in Cartesian space, thereby possibly impeding the development of intuitive physical relationships. For example, satellite trajectories appear extremely distorted on a (B, L) plot relative to a (R, λ) plot. The (R, λ) coordinate system is probably preferable to the (B, L) system for geocentric distances between about 3 and 6R_E and $\lambda < 70°$, since both coordinate systems have about the

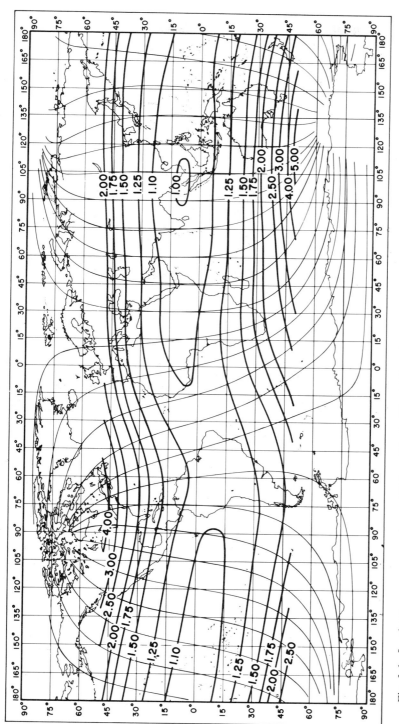

Fig. 3-6. *L*-value traces as mapped on a 500-km altitude ($R = 1.08$) surface and projected on the Earth's surface (after Dudziak *et al.*, 1963).

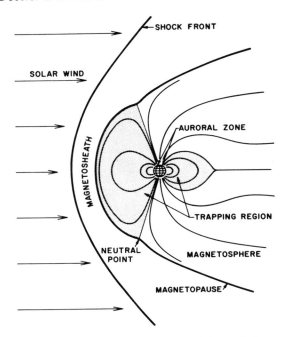

Fig. 3-7. Illustrative sketch showing the configuration of the radiation trapped in the geomagnetic field. The day-night asymmetry, caused by the distortion of the geomagnetic field by the solar wind, implies that the gradient and centrifugal-force guiding-center drift on the day side is much smaller than at night. This figure is based principally on the experimental work of Freeman *et al.* (1963), O'Brien (1963a), O'Brien and Taylor (1964), and the theoretical model of Dessler and Juday (1964). See Section 8.5 for a discussion of the effect of the solar wind on the geomagnetic field and definitions of the terms used in this figure.

same accuracy ($\sim$1 per cent). Beyond $6R_E$ and for geomagnetic latitudes above 70°, neither coordinate system can be expected to give physically meaningful results, as shown by O'Brien (1963a). The failure of the dipole-based coordinate systems is due to the distortion of the geomagnetic field by the solar wind (see Section 8.5). At high latitudes and at large geocentric distances, data should be presented with regard to the distortion of the geomagnetic field sketched in **Fig. 3-7** or **8-14**. However, the (B, L) system retains its usefulness for ordering data at low altitudes and high latitudes so that solar-wind-induced distortions may be detected.

3.2.3. Description of the Van Allen Radiation Belt

The Van Allen radiation consists almost wholly of electrons and protons. A very small flux of deuterons and tritons has been detected (Freden and White, 1962; Heckman and Armstrong, 1962), and, although none has yet been identified, it is possible that up to a few per cent of the total ionic flux is due to alpha particles (see Section 3.2.4).

The first spatial explorations of Van Allen radiations were made with shielded geiger tubes on Explorers 1, 3, and 4 (Van Allen et al., 1959c) and Sputniks 2 and 3 (Vernov and Chudakov, 1960). These satellites found regions of enhanced counting rates at latitudes near 50° and within ±40° of the equator, with a region of low counting rate between. When the space probe Pioneer 3 found that this distinction into two regions of high counting rate was present in the equatorial plane also, the two regions were called the inner and outer radiation belts, and the intermediate region of lower counting rate was called the "slot" (Van Allen and Frank, 1959a, b). This separation into two belts was a consequence of the fact that the early studies of the spatial extent were carried out with shielded geiger tubes that detected only the most energetic penetrating particles. Some of the early assumptions made as to the type of particles and their spectra were incorrect and led to gross errors in the values for the particle flux and its spatial configuration, particularly for electrons.

The most penetrating components of the radiation belt have been shown to consist of the following: (1) a hard-proton component (the proton belt) centered at approximately 10×10^3 km from the Earth's magnetic axis, or at $L \approx 1.5$ (Freden and White, 1959; McIlwain, 1959; Van Allen, 1959; Fan et al., 1960); and (2) an electron component (the electron belt) centered at approximately 22×10^3 km from the Earth's magnetic axis, or at $L \approx 3.5$ (Van Allen, 1959; Vernov et al., 1959; Walt et al., 1960; Fan et al., 1960; Arnoldy et al., 1960a). The electron belt extends through the region occupied by the proton belt (Holly and Johnson, 1960). Lower-energy radiation that cannot penetrate ~1 gm/cm² but can penetrate ~1 mg/cm² is present throughout the entire trapping region, shown in **Fig. 3-7**.

3.2.4. Van Allen Ions

Studies with nuclear emulsions (Freden and White, 1959) and with scintillators (Davis and Williamson, 1963) have proved that energetic ions, principally protons, are durably trapped in the geomagnetic field. Measurements have been made of trapped protons with energy E_p between ~100 kev and 700 Mev, and refined techniques will presumably extend the range of measured particles to both higher and lower energies. The protons are the most penetrating natural component in the inner zone and contribute most of the particle kinetic-energy density in the outer zone.

The relative composition of trapped ions has been determined only for the energetic particles in the inner zone from analysis of the tracks they have left in recovered nuclear emulsions flown through the region. Freden and White (1960) showed that there were very few penetrating particles heavier than protons in the inner zone. Hence, determination of the exact composition is difficult because of possible contamination by heavy particles produced by the primary protons that strike the payload itself.

Two emulsion groups have given attention to this problem (Freden and White, 1960; Heckman and Armstrong, 1962). They have used different criteria for the selection of tracks to be studied, and hence their data refer to somewhat different energy ranges. Ignoring these differences, we have grouped all the data together for approximate energy intervals in Table 3-1.

TABLE 3-1

RELATIVE PROPORTIONS OF HEAVY ENERGETIC IONS
TRAPPED IN THE INNER ZONE

Particle		Number of Tracks	Percentage
Proton	$(E > 35 \text{ Mev})$	1270	99.
Deuteron	$(E > 50 \text{ Mev})$	6	~ 0.5
Triton	$(E > 60 \text{ Mev})$	5	~ 0.5
$Z \geqq 2$	$(E > 125 \text{ Mev})$	None	~ 0.0

According to Freden and White (1960) the observed intensity of tritons was essentially what they would predict if all the tritons were secondary products of nuclear interactions of primary trapped protons with atmospheric constituents. It appears that the observed flux of trapped deuterons can be explained in the same way.

The spatial distribution of trapped protons is sketched in **Fig. 3-8** for two ranges of energy, viz. "low energy" or 100 kev $< E_p <$ 4 Mev, and "high energy" or $E_p >$ 40 Mev. These are the ranges studied by a scintillation counter on Explorer 12 (Davis and Williamson, 1963) and by geiger counters on Explorer 4 and other detectors on Explorer 14, Relay, etc. (McIlwain, 1963). The peak flux of the low-energy trapped protons, as shown in **Fig. 3-8** at $L \approx 4$, is $J(100 \text{ kev} < E_p < 4 \text{ Mev}) \approx 10^8$ protons/cm²-sec. The peak flux of more energetic protons at $L \approx 1.5$ in the equatorial plane is $J(E_p > 40 \text{ Mev}) \approx 3 \times 10^4$ protons/cm²-sec, as first estimated by Van Allen (1959).

The outermost high-energy ($E_p >$ 40 Mev) proton-flux contour delimits the region generally referred to as the inner zone of the radiation belt; the remainder of the belt is often called the outer zone. The proton-flux contours tend to be symmetrical about the integral-invariant equator. Since the geomagnetic field is not centered about the Earth's spin axis, the heights of the contours above the

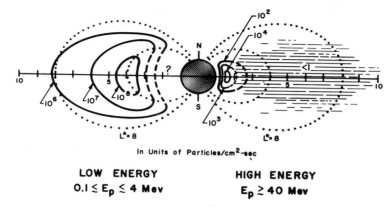

In Units of Particles/cm²-sec

LOW ENERGY   **HIGH ENERGY**

$0.1 \lesssim E_p \lesssim 4$ Mev $E_p \geq 40$ Mev

Fig. 3-8. Sketch of the omnidirectional fluxes of protons of relatively low energy ($0.1 < E_p < 4$ Mev) and relatively high energy ($E_p > 40$ Mev). These fluxes were derived from work of Davis and Williamson (1963), Van Allen (1959), and McIlwain (1963). The high-energy fluxes in the region beyond about 13,000 km ($L \approx 2.1$) indicated by horizontal lines undergo time variations (see Fig. 3-10). Also, the lower-energy fluxes at $L > 3$ change during magnetic storms (Davis and Williamson, 1963).

Earth's surface are a function of longitude. The contours closer than 1×10^4 km from the Earth's center are probably correct within a factor of 2; beyond about 1×10^4 km they may fluctuate as much as a factor of 10.

Very many observations in other energy ranges with other detectors also provide information on trapped protons. For example, a geiger-counter telescope on Explorer 6 gave the radial distribution of protons with $E_p > 70$ Mev (Fan *et al.*, 1960). Several nuclear-emulsion measurements (e.g., Freden and White, 1962) gave the most detail on the energy spectra of the energetic component in the inner zone, while another (Naugle and Kniffen, 1963) provided evidence of a softening proton spectrum with increasing L.

Proton flux contours based on the work of Van Allen (1959) and McIlwain (1963) are shown in **Fig. 3-9**. McIlwain (1964) has found that, beyond a geocentric distance of 1.3×10^4 km ($L \approx 2.1$), the energetic proton flux can be perturbed by nonadiabatic processes. **Fig. 3-10** shows that, following a large magnetic storm on September 23, 1963, the flux of trapped protons with $E_p > 34$ Mev decreased by more than a factor of 5 at $L = 2.4$ and by lesser amounts at lower values of L, with no effect noticeable at $L = 2.1$. The detailed mechanism by which such a change might occur is not well understood. An attractive possibility is the magnetospheric convection process, which could increase markedly during magnetically disturbed times (Axford and Hines, 1961). These perturbations might cause "bumps" and structure in the outer part of the energetic proton belt, such as that found by McIlwain (1964) at $L = 2.2$.

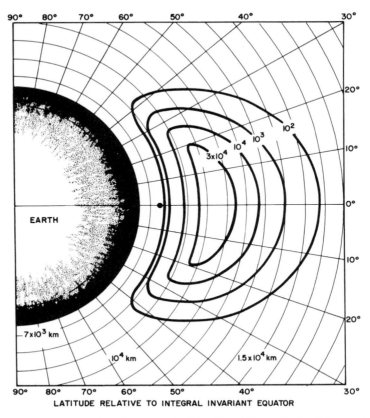

Fig. 3-9. Energetic proton flux (inner zone) of the Van Allen radiation. The numbers identify flux contours of protons with energies greater than about 35 Mev in protons/cm²-sec. The dot at the lower edge of the belt is to be put at the altitudes indicated in Fig. 3-11a to take into account the variations in the altitude and latitude of the belt as a function of longitude. As shown, the altitude of the belt is appropriate for 210° E longitude. The proton flux beyond about 1.3×10^4 km undergoes time variations.

The location of the integral-invariant equator relative to geographic coordinates is shown in **Fig. 3-11**. Altitudes of the base of the radiation belt at various positions around the integral-invariant equator are expressed in kilometers by the numbers at the arrows in **Fig. 3-11a**. The location of the integral-invariant equator and the altitudes were obtained from the high-order spherical harmonic analysis of the geomagnetic field carried out by Jensen *et al.* (1960). **Figure 3-11a** indicates the altitude at the bottom of the radiation belt, where the counting rate is just above cosmic-ray background. The field strength here is $B = 0.220$ gauss (Yoshida *et al.*, 1960). Similarly **Fig. 3-11b** indicates the altitudes along the integral-invariant equator where the flux of protons with energies

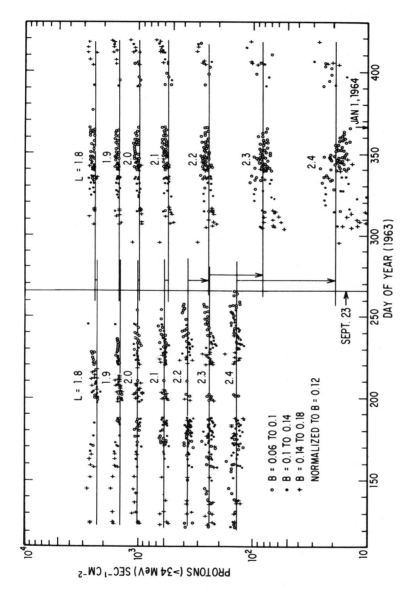

Fig. 3-10. Reduction of the flux of energetic ($E_p > 34$ Mev) trapped protons following the great magnetic storm on September 23, 1963 (McIlwain, 1964).

greater than 40 Mev is 10^2 protons/cm²-sec (about 50 times cosmic-ray background). The field strength here is 0.200 gauss.

Figure 3-12 shows the increase in the proton flux as a function of altitude above the bottom of the radiation belt at the integral-invariant equator. This figure was drawn utilizing the data presented by Yoshida *et al.* (1960) and the spherical harmonic analysis of Jensen *et al.* (1960). The bottom of the radiation belt can be located with the aid of **Fig. 3-11a**. The proton flux at a given altitude and longitude along the integral-invariant equator can be found by using **Figs. 3-11a** and **3-12**. As an example, let us find the proton flux at an altitude of 1500

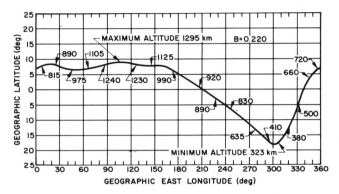

a. Field strength of 0.220 gauss. The numbers are the altitudes in kilometers where the proton flux is barely detectable above cosmic-ray background.

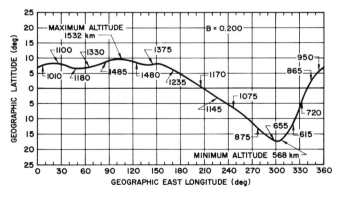

b. Field strength of 0.200 gauss. The numbers are the altitudes in kilometers where the flux is 10^2 protons/cm²-sec above 40 Mev.

Fig. 3-11. Location and altitude of the integral-invariant equator with respect to geographic coordinates. Altitudes shown should be correct to within ±25 km.

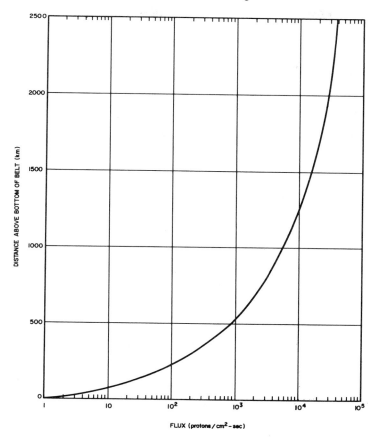

FLUX (protons / cm² - sec)

Fig. 3-12. Distribution of protons, with energies greater than about 35 Mev, above the bottom of the radiation belt near the integral-invariant equator. To obtain the altitude at which a given flux occurs at a given longitude, add the altitude indicated here to that shown in Fig. 3-11a. Flux values shown on this graph should be correct to within a factor of 2.

km at 45° E. From **Fig. 3-11a**, we find that at 45° E the bottom of the radiation belt is 975 km above the Earth's surface. Then from **Fig. 3-12** we see that, at $1500 - 975 = 525$ km above the bottom of the radiation belt (or 1500 km above the Earth's surface at 45° E), the proton flux is 1.0×10^3 protons/cm²-sec.

The low-energy (100 kev $< E_p < 4$ Mev) trapped protons are found in the equatorial plane right out to the boundary of the ordered geomagnetic field (Davis and Williamson, 1963). Their spectrum gradually softens (or steepens) as L increases, and some such general tendency summarizes very crudely all the trapped protons, including those of higher energies at smaller L values.

The proton flux and spectrum at $L \approx 1.4$ is of the form

$$J(E_p)dE \propto E_p^{-1.8}dE$$

for 75 Mev $< E_p < 700$ Mev (Freden and White, 1959). At $L \approx 1.53$, $B = 0.209$ gauss, the spectrum is given by

$$J(E_p)dE \propto E_p^{-1.7 \pm 0.3}dE$$

for 40 Mev $< E_p < 100$ Mev, and at $L = 1.79$, $B = 0.23$ gauss,

$$J(E_p)dE \propto E_p^{-4.5 \pm 0.5}dE$$

for 10 Mev $< E_p < 50$ Mev (Naugle and Kniffen, 1963). At still larger values of L, the spectrum over the range 100 kev $< E_p < 4$ Mev has been summarized (Davis and Williamson, 1963) as of the form

$$J(E_p)dE \propto \exp\left(\frac{-E}{E_0}\right)dE,$$

where $E_0 = 400$ kev at $L \approx 2.8$, $E_0 = 120$ kev at $L \approx 5.0$, and $E_0 = 64$ kev at $L \approx 6.1$. Indeed, McIlwain and Pizzella (1963) have fitted an empirical relation to all the existing proton spectral measurements by using a similar exponential spectral shape, and by writing

$$E_0 = (306 \pm 28)L^{-5.2 \pm 0.2}\text{Mev}.$$

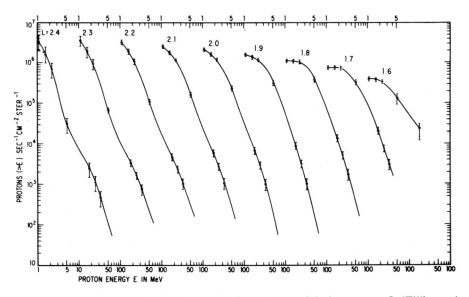

Fig. 3-13. Energy spectra of trapped protons in the equatorial plane versus L (Fillius and McIlwain, 1964).

The numerical values were derived from Explorer 4 data at $L < 2$, but they are roughly consistent with the above data out to $L \approx 6$. However, since this empirical relation does not include a lower-energy component in the inner zone or make allowance for temporal variations, it is clearly imperfect. But it provides a useful relation in a branch of study that, at this time, lacks any quantitative theory to give it complete coherence.

The most comprehensive summary of penetrating proton energy spectra for $L < 2.2$ has been prepared by Fillius and McIlwain (1964), and this summary is shown in **Fig. 3-13**.

3.2.5. Van Allen Electrons

Measurements have been made of trapped electrons with energy (E_e) between ~ 1 kev and ~ 5 Mev, although the existing measurements for $E_e \lesssim 10$ kev are unsatisfactorily sparse when one considers the roles such electrons play in many geophysical phenomena such as auroras. In this section we will treat only Van Allen or natural electrons, even though at $L \sim 1.5$ they are now a relatively minor constituent compared to artificially injected electrons (see Section 3.2.6). Experimental study of Van Allen electrons, always difficult because of the great penetrating power of the energetic protons in the inner zone, has now become very much more difficult. For about the next ten years in the inner zone, the natural and artificially injected electrons will be thoroughly mixed, and they carry no labels for the experimentalist to distinguish between them. Unfortunately, the Van Allen electrons had not been well studied before the bomb electrons were injected.

The spatial distribution of electrons in a low-energy ($E_e < 1$ Mev) range occupies the whole of the magnetospheric trapping region shown in **Fig. 3-7**; they persist in appreciable fluxes out to the boundary of the ordered geomagnetic field (Rosser *et al.,* 1962). Since this boundary is also controlled by solarwind effects, its location is a function of local time, and so, too, is the spatial distribution of the low-energy electrons. Such a local-time dependence was found by O'Brien (1963a) with Injun 1 at an altitude of ~ 1000 km. The flux of trapped electrons with $E_e > 40$ kev is roughly constant at this altitude over North America up to a high northern invariant latitude λ beyond which it becomes undetectable. The value of λ was $\sim 69°$ at local night and $\sim 75°$ at local noon. These invariant latitudes correspond to $L^* \sim 8$ and $L^* \sim 15$ respectively, but of course the very existence of this diurnal effect causes L to lose its simple connotation of a geocentric radial distance for $L > 6$. (Therefore, we have labeled L values greater than 6 as L^*.) This diurnal variation was also studied later with Alouette data (McDiarmid and Burrows, 1964; Frank *et al.,* 1964a) and confirmed.

Such local-time studies were extended to high altitudes with Explorers 12 and 14 (Frank *et al.*, 1963). We can now sketch the trapping region for low-energy electrons throughout the magnetosphere in the midday-midnight meridional plane, as shown in **Fig. 3-7**. The view in the equatorial plane is complex and dependent more on the distance from the ecliptic plane at large radial distances.

Not only are there systematic local-time variations in the trapped electrons at large values of L, but there are also great changes in universal time in electron fluxes and energy spectra down to $L \approx 2$. These changes, which are particularly large during large magnetic storms, are so great as to render any average electron distribution meaningless at $L > 3$. In general, the flux of electrons in the equatorial plane at $3 < L < 6$ varies between the order of 10^6 to 10^8 electrons/cm²-sec for $E_e > 40$ kev and between $\sim 10^3$ and 10^6 electrons/cm²-sec for $E_e > 1.5$ Mev (Frank *et al.*, 1964b). The spectra generally are steepened at larger values of L. During large magnetic storms, the lower-energy component increases in intensity, but the higher-energy ($E_e > 1.5$ Mev) component initially decreases, then increases to above its pre-storm value in a day or so, and after that gradually recovers to its pre-storm value over a few days. (See Freeman, 1964, for a more detailed discussion of these time variations.) The changes in flux need not necessarily imply that any of these same trapped particles were ever precipitated into the atmosphere. Instead it may well be true that the trapped electrons are simply energized and de-energized (e.g., by the ring-current mechanism proposed by Dessler and Karplus, 1961).

Great confusion persisted for several years after the discovery of the radiation belt because of a common misinterpretation of the cause of high counting rates of shielded geiger counters in the outer radiation zone. It was often assumed that the principal contribution to these rates came from bremsstrahlung from low-energy ($E_e > 30$ kev) electrons, and consequently the fluxes of these particles were quoted as $\sim 10^{11}$ electrons/cm²-sec. Considerable evidence that this assumption was invalid was presented by Gringauz *et al.* (1960) and Dessler (1960); the high flux value was subsequently proved to be wrong by measurements with an electron spectrometer on Explorer 12 (O'Brien *et al.*, 1962) that showed that the peak flux was of order 10^8 electrons/cm²-sec and that the high counting rates of the early experiments were caused by direct penetration of the shielding by energetic ($E_e > 1.5$ Mev) electrons in fluxes of the order 10^5 electrons/cm²-sec. Many subsequent experiments have confirmed these Explorer 12 results. (See review by Farley, 1963, for additional details.)

The energy spectra of electrons in the inner zone were not measured very accurately prior to the artificial injection of electrons (see Section 3.2.6). The available data on inner zone electron spectra are gathered in **Fig. 3-14** (Imhof *et al.*, 1963). Measurements with Explorer 4 of the flux of electrons with energy

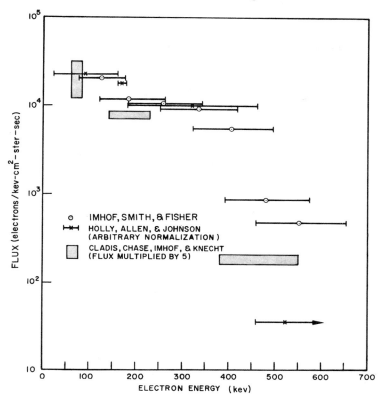

Fig. 3-14. Normalized electron spectra measured in the inner zone and at low altitudes in the outer zone (after Imhof *et al.*, 1963).

above ~600 kev (McIlwain, private communication) may be interpreted as indicating that the spectrum is richer in such high-energy electrons than **Fig. 3-14** would indicate.

Peak fluxes in the heart of the inner zone at $L \approx 1.4$ to 1.5 have been assessed (O'Brien, 1963b) as

$$J(E_e > 40 \text{ kev}) \approx 10^8 \text{ electrons/cm}^2\text{-sec-sterad}$$

and

$$J(E_e > 600 \text{ kev}) \approx 10^6 \text{ electrons/cm}^2\text{-sec-sterad} .$$

These peak values are for fluxes perpendicular to the magnetic field. They are uncertain to a factor of at least 3. At higher altitudes, better spectral measurements of Van Allen electrons are easier to make because the "background" flux of penetrating protons is much less. The measurements show that considerable spectral changes occur with time, particularly at times of magnetic storms, so

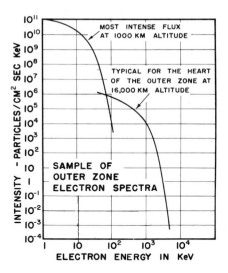

Fig. 3-15. Comparison of a typical electron spectrum for the heart of the outer zone with the spectrum of the most intense natural electron flux yet encountered, which was found at an altitude of 1000 km near the auroral zone by the satellite Injun I.

that simple generalizations should be treated with care. One can state that, for $L > 2$, the spectrum tends to become softer or steeper as L increases. (This generalization may also apply to $1 < L < 3$, but the measurements are inadequate to test it.) Some outer-zone spectral measurements are illustrated in **Fig. 3-15**. It is worth comment here that the energy spectra of electrons that cause auroras are generally much softer than the spectra of trapped electrons (McIlwain, 1960).

3.2.6. Starfish Radiation

The characteristic of Van Allen radiation that makes its theoretical and experimental study particularly difficult is that it is a natural and uncontrollable phenomenon. Its present properties are a consequence of past events and of a quasi-equilibrium between its sources and its losses. There is no known method by which one can separate, and study independently, the loss and source process of the natural radiation. It is obvious, therefore, that one can gain valuable information if one can provide and control artificial source and/or loss mechanisms. Suggestions have been made that large area satellites (such as Echoes but with thicker skins) be used to scatter and absorb trapped particles and so increase their loss rate (Singer, 1959). However, because of the eccentric dipole magnetic moment of the Earth, such a scheme is not practical.

A simpler approach is to change the source, i.e., to inject particles into trapped orbits. Two techniques of doing this have been discussed. The first is to inject positrons by putting into orbit an appropriately radioactive object (Hones,

1964). This approach is attractive because the flux of Van Allen positrons is apparently negligible (less than 10^{-9} of the electron flux, Peterson, 1964), so that one could readily distinguish between natural and artificially injected particles. But this technique has not been used. The second technique, which has been used, is the artificial injection of fission fragments from nuclear explosions at such high altitudes that their β-decay electrons may be trapped.

To date there have been at least seven occasions when a nuclear device was exploded at a sufficiently high altitude to inject radiation in the magnetosphere that endured for at least a few days (see review by Hess, 1964). The Starfish explosion of July 9, 1962, introduced energetic electrons that will remain trapped for about ten years. The U.S. Hardtack explosions of the megaton devices Teak and Orange at 80 km in 1958 produced some satellite-detected radiation locally. A Russian device exploded late in 1961 may have produced some effects, and three Russian devices exploded late in 1962 certainly did. The three Argus explosions of 1958 were small and produced observable radiation belts only for a few weeks.

An unfortunate feature of such tests is that they contaminate the radiation zones because one cannot distinguish between natural and artificially injected electrons. Before the positron technique is used there should be extremely careful measurements of the flux of naturally trapped positrons.

In order that a charged particle be durably trapped, it must be put into the geomagnetic field at any location in such a trajectory that its velocity vector lies outside the loss cone. An efficient method of doing so is to have an unstable parent particle carried to a high altitude where it can decay. Suitable parent particles are neutrons and fission fragments, and one can produce these in fission and fusion explosions. These explosions can inject particles of different types, such as α particles, or low-energy electrons and protons from neutron decay. Neutrons from such explosions populate the entire magnetosphere along their allowed trajectories, since they are uncharged and free to travel through the geomagnetic field (Crain and Tamarkin, 1961; Foderaro, 1964). However, the most dramatic effect is the injection of electrons from radioactive decay of fission debris.

Fission fragments consist of many different isotopes (e.g., Sr^{90}), which are generally neutron-rich and consequently unstable. The β particles or electrons that result from a fission explosion come from this mixture of isotopes, which decay with different lifetimes and yield a variety of energy spectra. We now group all the contributions together and discuss the β particles that result from a fission explosion at the time $t = 0$ seconds.

From a 1-kiloton fission explosion, the energy released as kinetic energy of the fragments is around 4×10^{19} ergs. There are about 10^{23} fission fragments emitted per kiloton, and about six fission electrons per fragment. Thus, from 1 kiloton one expects a total of about 5×10^{23} fission electrons, of which about one-sixth are given off in the first second and the remainder at a rate proportional to $t^{-1.2}$, where t is in seconds (Johnson and Dyce, 1960). The fragments therefore are an active source for hours after the detonation. They travel away from the detonation points at speeds of about 500 km/sec. The distance they travel is dependent on the development of the "bubble" that contains them, and on whether they are charged or neutral (Hess, 1964).

The equilibrium spectrum of fission electrons in units of β particles per fission has the form (Carter *et al.,* 1959)

$$N(E)dE = 3.88 \exp(-0.575E - 0.055E^2) \, dE$$

for the range $1 < E < 7$, where E is the electron energy in Mev. It has been suggested (Hess, 1964) that the spectrum from a device such as Starfish may be softer at large distances, owing to Fermi deceleration within the bubble. Observations of the U.S.S.R. artificial belts lend support to the existence of such softer spectra.

Some of the fission-decay electrons are injected promptly into trapped orbits, but many populate the loss cone and plunge into the atmosphere, both below the detonation point and in the conjugate area at the other end of the geomagnetic field lines that pass through the detonation region. In the conjugate area they produce artificial auroras. With Starfish these were extremely intense and lasted for hours, owing to continual supply of fission electrons from (*a*) fission fragments in the detonation regions, (*b*) fission fragments in the conjugate area, and perhaps (*c*) locally trapped, charged fission fragments.

McIlwain (1963) shows the spatial distribution of electrons with $E_e > 5$ Mev as measured some months after Starfish and some weeks after the U.S.S.R. detonations. Since there were no adequate measurements of such energetic electrons in this region prior to Starfish, it is not certain that most of the particles are artificially injected. Most scientists would agree that they probably are artificial except perhaps at $L > 2.5$.

The Starfish and U.S.S.R. belts have given valuable quantitative information on the rate of loss of trapped electrons over the range $L < 2$. Studies at $L > 2$ have been somewhat confused because there is controversial disagreement among various estimates of the extent of Starfish at $L > 2$. However, data from the Russian explosions allows conclusions to be drawn on the electron loss rate at large L, independent of the Starfish arguments. Walt and MacDonald (1964) have studied the loss of trapped electrons from these explosions. They conclude that atmospheric scattering controls the loss of electrons for $L < 1.25$ and of protons for $L < 1.4$. At larger L values the loss rate is faster than predicted by atmo-

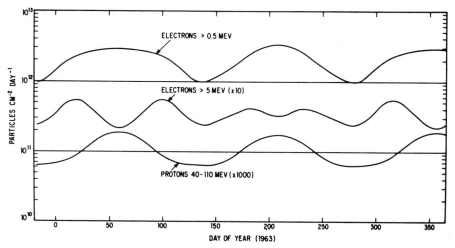

PARTICLES CM⁻² DAY⁻¹

ELECTRONS > 0.5 MEV

ELECTRONS > 5 MEV (×10)

PROTONS 40-110 MEV (×1000)

DAY OF YEAR (1963)

Fig. 3-16. Daily radiation doses encountered by the Relay 1 satellite, whose geocentric apogee distance was 2.07 Earth radii, perigeè distance 1.21 Earth radii, and inclination 47.5° (McIlwain *et al.,* 1964).

spheric scattering alone, indicating the presence of some additional process. As mentioned earlier, large-scale magnetospheric convection (Gold, 1959; Axford and Hines, 1961; Fejer, 1964) may provide the additional mechanism. At the present time, the flux of electrons from the Starfish radiation provides the major source of radiation for satellites in the inner zone. The integrated flux encountered in a typical satellite orbit is shown in **Fig. 3-16.**

3.3. SOLAR-FLARE COSMIC RADIATION

After the Van Allen and Starfish radiation belts, the next most intense known penetrating radiation is that from the few solar flares which eject high-energy protons and electrons and perhaps neutrons. Half an hour or more following the appearance of some large solar flares, protons and heavier nuclei with energies typically up to 200 Mev (Anderson *et al.,* 1959; Rothwell and McIlwain, 1959; Freier *et al.,* 1959; Biswas *et al.,* 1962) and electrons with energies up to 100 Mev (Meyer and Vogt, 1962) are detected at the Earth, usually in the polar regions inside the auroral zones. This radiation dies away with a time constant of one to three days. The solar-flare-proton events may be divided into two classes—those that contain relativistic protons and those that contain only nonrelativistic protons. As a working definition, relativistic events are those that are observable at sea level with appropriate instruments, i.e., those events with proton energies greater than 1 Bev. The protons in the nonrelativistic events are all stopped high in the Earth's atmosphere and produce no detectable radiation at the Earth's surface. There appears to be a gradual transition between the relativistic and the nonrelativistic events. No particular significance should be placed on the 1-Bev dividing point chosen here. The relativistic and nonrelativistic events are separated in this section solely on the basis that one can be detected at ground level while the other cannot.

Equipment capable of detecting these relativistic solar-flare events has been in operation since 1937. During the following 27 years, 12 events occurred that were readily detectable at ground level (McCracken and Palmeira, 1960; Carmichael, 1962). The largest event was that of February 1956, in which it has been estimated (Meyer et al., 1956) that the flux above 3 Bev was about 3×10^2 times normal cosmic-ray intensity. The occurrence of relativistic events shows no obvious correlation with the solar cycle, although there are hardly enough data to warrant a definite conclusion at the present time. The 12 relativistic solar-flare-proton events that have been observed are listed below.

Event	Date	Event	Date
1	February 28, 1942	7	May 4, 1960
2	March 7, 1942	8	September 3, 1960
3	July 25, 1946	9	November 12, 1960
4	November 19, 1949	10	November 15, 1960
5	February 23, 1956	11	July 18, 1961
6	July 17, 1959	12	July 20, 1961

The nonrelativistic particle radiation associated with solar flares occurs principally during the years of sunspot maximum. The data for **Fig. 3-17**, which show the number of solar-flare cosmic-ray events per year, have been obtained from experiments that monitor flare-radiation ionospheric effects (Bailey, 1959; Little and Leinbach, 1959). The events have been arbitrarily divided into two classes—big events that are characterized by total time-integrated fluxes above 30 Mev of more than about 10^8 particles/cm^2, and small ones characterized by time-integrated fluxes of less than about 10^8 particles/cm^2.

It has been shown for the November 12, 1960, flare that He, C, N, O, and Ne nuclei (Biswas et al., 1962) and electrons (Meyer and Vogt, 1962) were accelerated in addition to protons. The relative proportion of these constituents is highly variable from flare to flare (Ney and Stein, 1962). The relative abundance of solar-flare cosmic-radiation nuclei is given in Table 3-2 and compared with galactic cosmic radiation, the universal abundance of elements, and the spectroscopic composition of the sun. In addition to these constituents that have been detected, it is expected that for the more energetic and certainly for the relativistic solar-flare events, energetic neutrons will be produced (Lingenfelter and Flamm, 1964; Haymes, 1964).

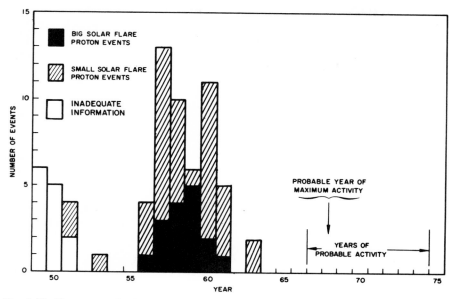

Fig. 3-17. Frequency of solar-flare cosmic-ray impingement on the polar cap. These events have been arbitrarily divided into two classes: big events and small events, where the dividing line is set at a time-integrated flux of about 10^8 particles/cm²-sec above 30 Mev (after Bailey, 1964, and Webber, 1963).

TABLE 3-2

RELATIVE ABUNDANCES OF NUCLEI NORMALIZED TO A
BASE OF 1.0 FOR OXYGEN

(After Biswas & Fichtel, 1964)

Element	Solar-Flare Cosmic Rays	Sun	Universal Abundances	Galactic Cosmic Rays
$_1$H^1	700	1000.	1000.	350.
$_2$He	107 ± 14	~100.	~100.	50.
$_3$Li	. . .	<<0.001	<<0.001	0.3
$_4$Be $_5$B	<0.02	<<0.001	<<0.001	0.8
$_6$C	0.59 ± 0.07	0.6	0.3	1.8
$_7$N	0.19 ± 0.04	0.1	0.2	≤0.8
$_8$O	1.0	1.0	1.0	1.0
$_9$F	<0.03	<<0.001	<<0.001	≤0.1
$_{10}$Ne	0.13 ± 0.02	?	0.40	0.30
$_{11}$Na	. . .	0.002	0.001	0.19
$_{12}$Mg	0.043 ± 0.011	0.027	0.042	0.32
$_{13}$Al	. . .	0.002	0.002	0.06
$_{14}$Si	0.033 ± 0.011	0.035	0.046	0.12
$_{15}$P–$_{21}$Sc	0.057 ± 0.017	0.032	0.027	0.13
$_{22}$Ti–$_{28}$Ni	≤0.02	0.006	0.030	0.28

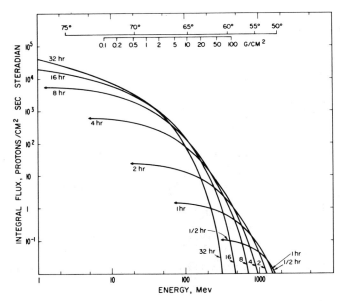

Fig. 3-18. Idealized time history of the integral-energy spectrum of solar-flare cosmic rays for a typical large event (Bailey, 1962).

The time history of a typical slow-rise, large solar-flare event according to Bailey (1962) is shown in **Fig. 3-18**. The variations in time and flux characteristics from flare to flare are extremely large, with the flux for the rapid-rise events reaching a peak ~30 minutes after the flare.

The time history of a solar-flare event is controlled by the flare and by propagation conditions for the flare particles through interplanetary space. The principal controlling factor in interplanetary space is the interplanetary magnetic field. McCracken (1962) was able to show that the interplanetary field had properties consistent with those predicted by Parker (1961b)—a continuous solar wind which leads to a spiral solar magnetic field pervading interplanetary space.

3.4. GALACTIC COSMIC RADIATION

Galactic cosmic radiation consists of stripped atoms (nuclei), electrons, and positrons moving with relativistic velocities obtained outside the solar system. The relative abundances of cosmic-ray nuclei are compared in Table 3-2 with the relative abundances in the solar-flare cosmic radiation, in the sun, and in the universe. As discussed by Biswas and Fichtel (1964), the galactic cosmic radiation abundances are very different from the others. The anomalously large relative abundance of the light elements Li, Be, and B is understood to be due to production of these elements by fragmentation of the heavier nuclei as they traverse, on the average, $\sim$3 g/cm² of interstellar matter before they reach the Earth. However, the galactic cosmic rays are also relatively richer in the heavier nuclei; the cause of this is not understood.

The cosmic-radiation-proton integral spectrum is shown in **Fig. 3-19** (Barrett *et al.*, 1952; McDonald, 1959). The nearly flat portion of the curve between 10^8 and 10^9 ev indicates that almost no protons have energies in this range, and that their energies lie almost entirely above 10^9 ev. The energy distribution for nuclei other than protons is, in a relative sense, the same as that shown in **Fig. 3-19**; the absolute value for the fluxes of heavier particles must, of course, be corrected for the relative abundances as shown in Table 3-2. (The flux scale should be changed in direct proportion to the relative abundances shown in Table 3-2, and the energy scale must be regarded as the energy per nucleon, where the number of nucleons in a nucleus is equal to the atomic weight or the sum of the number of protons and neutrons making up the nucleus.) The velocity distribution is essentially isotropic. The cosmic radiation with energies below about 5 Bev undergoes a variation with sunspot cycle; specifically, the low-energy end of the cosmic-ray spectrum is depleted during sunspot maximum. The change over the sunspot cycle is indicated in **Fig. 3-19**.

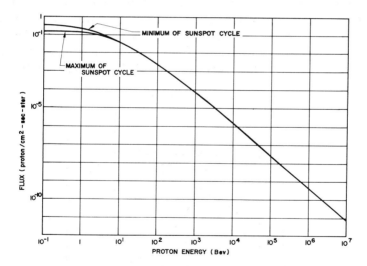

Fig. 3-19. Integral-cosmic-ray energy spectrum at extremes of the sunspot cycle. Space-probe measurements give a flux value of approximately 0.2 particle/cm²-sec-sterad above about 40 Mev near sunspot maximum; this value should increase by a factor of about 2.5 near sunspot minimum.

The kinetic energy of a particle of rest mass m_0 moving with a velocity v is given by

$$E = m_0 c^2 \left[\frac{1}{(1 - v^2/c^2)^{1/2}} - 1 \right],$$

where c is the velocity of light. When $v \ll c$, this expression reduces to $E = \frac{1}{2} m_0 v^2$. The momentum of the particle is given by $p = m_0 v / (1 - v^2/c^2)^{1/2}$, which reduces to the familiar expression $p = m_0 v$ when $v \ll c$.

Since the cosmic-radiation particles are electrically charged, their paths are bent by magnetic fields. The deflection of cosmic-radiation particles by the geomagnetic field prevents the lower-energy particles from reaching the Earth's surface at all, especially at low latitudes. The controlling factor is the ratio of the particle momentum to the particle charge, because the momentum is a measure of the particle's ability to resist change in direction of motion while the deflecting force is proportional to the charge on the particle. It is usual to express the momentum of cosmic-radiation particles in units of Bev/c, where 1 Bev = 10^9 ev and c is the velocity of light (1 Bev/$c = 0.53 \times 10^{-13}$ g-cm/sec). The effect of the dipole-like geomagnetic field in excluding particles from the Earth is shown in **Fig. 3-20** for protons and for alpha particles (Alpher, 1950); the latter are roughly similar in this respect to all the heavier cosmic-radiation particles. Near the geomagnetic equator, protons cannot reach the Earth unless they have momenta greater than about 14 Bev/c. The value depends on the angle at which the particles reach the Earth, and the value given here is for particles arriving vertically. At higher latitudes, particles with lower momenta are able to make their way through the magnetic field, as indicated in **Fig. 3-20**. It is clear

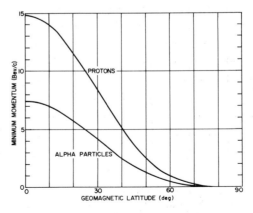

Fig. 3-20. Geomagnetic cut-off momenta for vertically incident protons and alpha particles at the Earth's surface for various geomagnetic latitudes. *Alpher (1950), reproduced with permission of J. Geophys. Research.*

that alpha particles (and heavier particles) do not require as much momentum to get through the magnetic field as do protons. In reality, there are such significant distortions of the geomagnetic field from that of a dipole that low-energy particles can enter the polar cap at lower latitudes than indicated by **Fig. 3-20**, particularly during magnetic storms.

In order to consider the ability of protons and heavier particles to penetrate the magnetic field on the same scale, the rigidity R is utilized—R is the ratio of the momentum to the charge and is defined by the expression

$$R = pc/Ze \, ,$$

where p is the momentum (in units of Bev/c), c is the velocity of light, and Ze is the charge on the particle; R is expressed in volts, which must not be confused with the units of energy, or electron volts. The rigidity is also frequently expressed in billions of volts, or Bv, which is the natural unit to use when the momenta are expressed in units of Bev/c rather than ev/c. The rigidity required

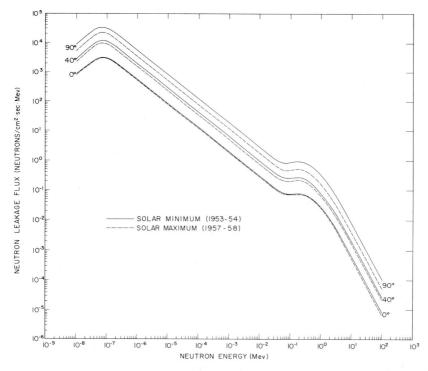

Fig. 3-21. Spectra of albedo neutrons generated by cosmic-radiation bombardment of the Earth's atmosphere (Lingenfelter, 1963). The curves apply to the top of the atmosphere for neutrons (~100 km).

of any particle to reach any geomagnetic latitude is given by the proton curve in **Fig. 3-20**, where the ordinate scale is regarded as a rigidity scale in units of Bv.

Primary cosmic rays that strike nuclei of atmospheric nitrogen and oxygen produce neutrons, some of which move away from the Earth; these neutrons are commonly called cosmic-ray-albedo neutrons. The albedo-neutron spectrum as calculated by Lingenfelter (1963) is shown in **Fig. 3-21**. The curves are in substantial agreement with the earlier results of Hess *et al.* (1961) above the atmosphere and at high energies. These albedo neutrons contribute to the Van Allen radiation when they decay (Hess, 1960). However, except at $L \leqq 1.25$ for electrons and $L \leqq 1.4$ for protons, their contribution is negligible (Walt and Mac-Donald, 1964). At smaller L values, their contribution to the trapped flux is likely to be significant.

Electrons were discovered in the cosmic radiation by Meyer and Vogt (1961) and Earl (1961). The flux of electrons with energies above several hundred Mev is of order 5×10^{-3} electrons/cm²-sec-sterad, or about one per cent of the proton flux. The ratio of positrons to electrons is found to be about one to two (DeShong *et al.,* 1964). The electrons and positrons could be produced in interstellar p–p collisions with comparable abundances, or in supernova explosions that would presumably produce predominantly electrons. The limited experimental results therefore tend to imply that the two postulated sources are of comparable importance.

3.5. PRECIPITATED AND AURORAL PARTICLES

A precipitated particle is one whose trajectory (i.e., local pitch angle) is such that it will tend to mirror below an altitude of 100 km. It is very likely, then, that it will be absorbed in the atmosphere, where it may produce ionization, auroras, etc. A precipitated particle need not necessarily ever have been a trapped or Van Allen particle with the same energy, and at high magnetic latitudes near the auroral zone it is probable that most precipitated electrons are freshly accelerated or energized (O'Brien and Taylor, 1964). The principal precipitation phenomena occur in the auroral zone. Particle precipitation grows monotonically less intense and less frequent toward the equator (O'Brien, 1964).

Rocket-borne and satellite-borne particle-radiation detectors have been flown through auroras (Davis *et al.,* 1960; McIlwain, 1960; O'Brien and Taylor, 1964; McDiarmid *et al.,* 1964; Sharp *et al.,* 1964) and have detected the presence of both energetic protons and electrons. On the basis of surface observations, Ohmholt (1959) argued that electrons supply the energy for the auroral light. The rocket measurements of Davis and McIlwain confirmed this conclusion. The measurements showed good correlation between positions of high auroral luminosity and high electron flux, and they also showed that the proton flux did not vary over distances of about 40 km even though the auroral luminosity varied greatly over that distance.

Most auroral electron fluxes have *e*-folding energies of the order of several kev, so that most of the energy is carried by electrons with energies less than a few tens of kev (McIlwain, 1960; Davis *et al.*, 1960; Sharp *et al.*, 1964; Frank *et al.*, 1964a). Auroras at lower latitudes tend to be caused by relatively harder electron fluxes. It was found that both the proton and electron flux were isotropic over the upper hemisphere, and that about 10 per cent of the particle flux was scattered back in an upward direction (O'Brien, 1964).

Both the electron and proton energy spectra were found to vary widely from experiment to experiment. The proton integral-energy spectrum ranged from E^{-4} to E^{-1} above about 100 km. (Here we use a power-law spectral relationship rather than the exponential form given above; the data are so sparse that either form fits the data equally well.) The flux above 100 kev seemed to lie generally between 10^4 and 10^6 protons/cm²-sec. The electron spectrum in a bright auroral arc was observed to consist of a nearly mono-energetic flux of approximately 2×10^{11} electrons/cm²-sec with energies near 6 kev (McIlwain, 1960). Other rocket observations in a quiescent auroral glow yielded electron integral-energy spectra which fit power-law distributions above 3 to 5 kev and range from $E^{-2.5}$ to E^{-1}. These power-law distributions should not be extrapolated below the stated lower energy limit. The flux in these quiescent displays varied between about 10^8 and 10^{10} electrons/cm²-sec. In active displays, the electron flux rose to $\sim 10^{12}$ electrons/cm²-sec. In quiescent displays, the electron flux between 30 ev and 1 kev was always less than 10^{10} electrons/cm²-sec (Davis *et al.*, 1960).

The results of O'Brien (1964) and O'Brien and Taylor (1964) show that (*a*) auroras occur at the high-latitude boundary of trapping as indicated in **Fig. 3-7**, and (*b*) the particle flux at altitudes up to ~ 1000 km is isotropic over the upper hemisphere above auroras. Important precipitation of electrons with higher energies (~ 50 kev) occur at latitudes below the aurora, and this precipitation must take place on closed magnetic field lines and be such as not to disturb appreciably the higher-energy (~ 1 Mev) trapped electrons.

It is of interest to determine whether auroral precipitation is more intense during the night than the day, and to find its local-time dependence. However, conflicting reports of its local-time dependence exist (Sharp *et al.*, 1964; Frank *et al.*, 1964a; McDiarmid and Burrows, 1964), perhaps in part because variations of particle flux with real time make such studies difficult. We are unable to conclude that any diurnal variation of precipitated radiation does, in fact, exist.

Precipitated protons have been little studied directly. Sharp *et al.* (1964) reports that proton precipitation appears less variable and "erratic" than electron precipitation. Ground-based photometric observations of auroras excited by electron bombardment and of Balmer emissions from proton bombardment indicate a tendency for proton precipitation at a lower latitude than electron precipitation prior to local midnight, with the opposite situation prevailing after local midnight (Stoffregen and Derblom, 1962).

It is now rather certain that the unmodified Van Allen radiation belt is not the source for the aurora. McIlwain (1960) pointed out that the spectra of auroral electrons and of Van Allen electrons are vastly different. An independent argument may be based on a comparison between the energy required to supply a bright auroral display and the energy stored in the radiation belt. Using the flux values given in this chapter, the total energy stored in electrons in the radiation belt is less than 10^{20} ergs. About 10^{17} ergs/sec are required for a bright aurora. Thus it appears that the entire Van Allen radiation belt would be expended in about 15 minutes in producing a bright aurora. Finally, O'Brien (1964) has shown that the fluxes of trapped electrons actually increase above an aurora, so that, rather than the radiation belt supplying the auroral radiation, it seems likely that auroral and Van Allen electrons have a common source.

A band of trapped soft radiation that probably is connected to the auroral zones has been observed beyond the normal Van Allen radiation belt on the night side of the Earth (Gringauz *et al.,* 1960; Freeman, 1964). A flux of about 10^9 electrons/cm²-sec with energies greater than 200 ev was measured between 8 and 11 Earth radii. A similar band of radiation has been detected with a higher energy threshold by Frank *et al.* (1964b). The radiation detected in the magnetosheath by Freeman *et al.* (1963) is probably not connected with the aurora in any direct way.

REFERENCES

Alfvén, H., and C. Fälthammar. 1963. *Cosmical Electrodynamics,* 2d ed. Oxford Press, London.

Alpher, R. A. 1950. "Theoretical Geomagnetic Effects in Cosmic Radiation," *J. Geophys. Research,* **55,** 437–71.

Anderson, K. A., R. Arnoldy, R. Hoffman, L. Peterson, and J. R. Winckler. 1959. "Observation of Low-Energy Solar Cosmic Rays from the Flare of 22 August 1958," *J. Geophys. Research,* **64,** 1133–47.

Arnoldy, R. L., R. A. Hoffman, and J. R. Winckler. 1960a. "Observations of the Van Allen Radiation Regions During August and September, 1959, Part I," *J. Geophys. Research,* **65,** 1361–76.

Arnoldy, R. L., R. A. Hoffman, and J. R. Winckler. 1960b. "Solar Cosmic Rays and Soft Radiation Observed at 5,000,000 Kilometers from the Earth," *J. Geophys. Research,* **65,** 3004–7.

Axford, W. I., and C. O. Hines. 1961. "A Unifying Theory of High-Latitude Geophysical Phenomena and Geomagnetic Storms," *Can. J. Phys.,* **39,** 1433–64.

Bailey, D. K. 1959. "Abnormal Ionization in the Lower Ionosphere Associated with Cosmic Ray Flux Enhancement," *Proc. I.R.E.,* **47,** 255–66.

Bailey, D. K. 1962. "Time Variations of the Energy Spectrum of Solar Cosmic Rays in Relation to the Radiation Hazard in Space," *J. Geophys. Research,* **67,** 391–96.

Bailey, D. K. 1964. "Polar Cap Absorption," *Planet. Space Sci.,* **12,** 495–541.

Barrett, P. H., L. M. Bollinger, G. Cocconi, Y. Eisenberg, K. Greisen. 1952. "Interpretations of Cosmic Ray Measurements Far Underground," *Rev. Modern Phys.,* **24,** 133–78.

Biswas, S., C. E. Fichtel, and D. E. Guss. 1962. "Study of the Hydrogen, Helium, and Heavy Nuclei in the Nov. 12, 1960, Solar Cosmic Ray Event," *Phys. Rev.,* **128,** 2756–71.

Biswas, S., and C. E. Fichtel. 1964. "Nuclear Composition and Rigidity Spectra of Solar Cosmic Rays," *Astrophys. J.,* **139,** 941–50.

Carmichael, H. 1962. "High Energy Solar-Particle Events," *Space Sci. Reviews,* **1,** 28–61.

Carter, R. E., F. Reines, J. J. Wagner, and M. E. Wyman. 1959. "Free Antineutrino Absorption Cross Section. II. Expected Cross Section from Measurements of Fission Fragment Electron Spectrum," *Phys. Rev.,* **113,** 280–86.

Cornwall, J. M. 1964. "Scattering of Energetic Trapped Electrons by Very-Low-Frequency Waves," *J. Geophys. Research,* **69,** 1251–58.

Crain, C. M., and P. Tamarkin. 1961. "A Note on the Cause of Sudden Ionization Anomalies in Regions Remote from High-Altitude Nuclear Bursts," *J. Geophys. Research,* **66,** 35–39.

Davis, L. R., O. E. Berg, and L. H. Meredith. 1960. "Direct Measurements of Particle Fluxes in and Near Auroras," in H. Kallmann Bijl, ed., *Space Research.* North-Holland Publishing Co., Amsterdam, pp. 721–35.

Davis, L. R., and J. M. Williamson. 1963. "Low Energy Trapped Protons," in W. Priester, ed., *Space Research III.* North-Holland Publishing Co., Amsterdam, pp. 365–75.

DeShong, J. A., R. H. Hildebrand, and P. Meyer. 1964. "Ratio of Electrons to Positrons in the Primary Cosmic Radiation," *Phys. Rev. Letters,* **12,** 3–6.

Dessler, A. J. 1960. "Discussion of Paper by R. L. Arnoldy, R. A. Hoffman, and J. R. Winckler, 'Observations of the Van Allen Radiation Regions During August and September, 1959, Part I,'" *J. Geophys. Research,* **65,** 3487–90.

Dessler, A. J., and Robert Karplus. 1961. "Some Effects of Diamagnetic Ring Currents on Van Allen Radiation," *J. Geophys. Research,* **66,** 2289–95.

Dessler, A. J., and R. D. Juday. 1964. "Configuration of Auroral Radiation in Space," to be submitted to *Planetary and Space Science.*

Dragt, A. J. 1961. "Effect of Hydromagnetic Waves on the Lifetime of Van Allen Radiation Protons," *J. Geophys. Research,* **66,** 1641–49.

Dudziak, W. F., D. D. Kleinecke, and T. J. Kostigen. 1963. "Graphic Displays of Geomagnetic Geometry," RM 63TMP-2, DASA 1372, General Electric Co., Santa Barbara, Calif.

Dungey, J. W. 1963a. "Loss of Van Allen Electrons Due to Whistlers," *Planetary and Space Sci.,* **11,** 591–96.

Dungey, J. W. 1963b. "The Effect of Quasi-Static Electric Fields on Van Allen Particles," *J. Geophys. Research,* **68,** 3540–41.

Earl, J. A. 1961. "Cloud-Chamber Observations of Primary Cosmic-Ray Electrons," *Phys. Rev. Letters,* **6,** 125–28.

Fan, C. Y., P. Meyer, and J. A. Simpson. 1960. "Trapped and Cosmic Radiation Measurements from Explorer VI," in H. Kallmann Bijl, ed., *Space Research.* North-Holland Publishing Co., Amsterdam, pp. 951–66.

Fan, C. Y., P. Meyer, and J. A. Simpson. 1961. "Dynamics and Structure of the Outer Radiation Belt," *J. Geophys. Research,* **66,** 2607–40.

Farley, T. A. 1963. "History of the Earth's Outer Radiation Zone," *Reviews of Geophysics,* **1,** 3.

Fejer, J. A. 1964. "Atmospheric Tides and Associated Magnetic Effects," *Reviews of Geophysics,* **2,** 275–309.

Fillius, R. Walker. 1963. "Satellite Instruments Using Solid State Detectors," Research Report SUI 63-26, Department of Physics and Astronomy, State University of Iowa, Iowa City. Unpublished thesis.

Fillius, R. Walker, and C. E. McIlwain. 1964. "Anomalous Energy Spectrum of Protons in the Earth's Radiation Belt," *Phys. Rev. Letters,* **12**, 609–12.

Foderaro, A. 1964. "Another Possible Explanation of Sudden Atmospheric Ionization in Regions Shadowed from High-Altitude Nuclear Bursts," *J. Geophys. Research,* **69**, 3137–40.

Frank, L. A., J. A. Van Allen, and E. Macagno. 1963. "Charged Particle Observations in the Earth's Outer Magnetosphere," *J. Geophys. Research,* **68**, 3543–54.

Frank, L. A., J. A. Van Allen, and J. D. Craven. 1964a. "Large Diurnal Variations of Geomagnetically Trapped and Precipitated Electrons Observed at Low Altitude," *J. Geophys. Research,* **69**, 3155–67.

Frank, L. A., J. A. Van Allen, and H. K. Hills. 1964b. "A Study of Charged Particles in the Earth's Outer Radiation Zone with Explorer 14," *J. Geophys. Research,* **69**, 2171–91.

Freden, S. C., and R. S. White. 1959. "Protons in the Earth's Magnetic Field," *Phys. Rev. Letters,* **3**, 9–11.

Freden, S. C., and R. S. White. 1960. "Particle Fluxes in the Inner Radiation Belt," *J. Geophys. Research,* **65**, 1377–83.

Freden, S. C., and R. S. White. 1962. "Trapped Protons and Cosmic-Ray Albedo Neutron Fluxes," *J. Geophys. Research,* **67**, 25–29.

Freeman, J. W., Jr. 1964. "The Morphology of the Electron Distribution in the Outer Zone and Near the Magnetospheric Boundary as Observed by Explorer 12," *J. Geophys. Research,* **69**, 1691–1723.

Freeman, J. W., Jr., J. A. Van Allen, and L. J. Cahill. 1963. "Explorer 12 Observations of the Magnetospheric Boundary and the Associated Solar Plasma on Sept. 13, 1961," *J. Geophys. Research,* **68**, 2121–30.

Freier, P. S., E. P. Ney, and J. R. Winckler. 1959. "Balloon Observations of Solar Cosmic Rays on March 26, 1958," *J. Geophys. Research,* **64**, 685–88.

Gold. T. 1959. "Motions of the Magnetosphere of the Earth," *J. Geophys. Research,* **64**, 1219–24.

Gringauz, K. I., V. G. Kurt, V. I. Moroz, and I. S. Shklovskii. 1960. "The Ionized Gas and Fast Electrons in the Vicinity of the Earth and in Interplanetary Space," *Doklady Akad. Nauk,* **132**, 1062–65 (translation in *Physics Express,* Oct. 1960, pp. 6–9).

Hamlin, D. A., R. Karplus, R. C. Vik, and K. M. Watson. 1961. "Mirror and Azimuthal Drift Frequencies for Geomagnetically Trapped Particles," *J. Geophys. Research,* **66**, 1–4.

Haymes, R. C. 1964. "Fast Neutrons in the Earth's Atmosphere. 2. Time Variations at High Altitudes," *J. Geophys. Research,* **69**, 853–59.

Heckman, H. H., and A. H. Armstrong. 1962. "Energy Spectrum of Geomagnetically-Trapped Protons," *J. Geophys. Research,* **67**, 1255–62.

Hess, W. N. 1960. "The Radiation Belt Produced by Neutrons Leaking Out of the Atmosphere of the Earth," *J. Geophys. Research,* **65**, 3107–15.

Hess, W. N. 1964. "The Effect of High-Altitude Explosions," in D. P. LeGalley and A. Rosen, eds., *Space Physics.* Wiley, New York, pp. 573–610.

Hess, W. N., E. H. Canfield, and R. E. Lingenfelter. 1961. "Cosmic Ray Neutron Demography," *J. Geophys. Research,* **66**, 665–77.

Holly, F. E., and R. G. Johnson. 1960. "Measurement of Radiation in the Lower Van Allen Belt," *J. Geophys. Research,* **65**, 771–72.

Hones, E. 1964. "On the Use of Positrons as Tracers to Study the Motions of Electrons Trapped in the Earth's Magnetosphere," *J. Geophys. Research,* **69**, 182–85.

Imhof, W. L., R. V. Smith, and P. C. Fisher. 1963. "Particle Flux Measurements from an Atlas Pod in the Lower Van Allen Belt," in W. Priester, ed., *Space Research III.* North-Holland Publishing Co., Amsterdam, pp. 438–46.

Jensen, D. C., R. W. Murray, and J. A. Welch, Jr. 1960. "Tables of Adiabatic Invariants for the Geomagnetic Field 1955.0," AFSWC-TN-60-8, Air Force Special Weapons Center, Kirtland Air Force Base, New Mexico.

Johnson, G., and R. Dyce. 1960. Stanford Research Institute Report, July 1960.

Lingenfelter, R. E. 1963. "The Cosmic-Ray Neutron Leakage Flux," *J. Geophys. Research,* **68,** 5633–39.

Lingenfelter, R. E., and E. J. Flamm. 1964. "Solar Neutrons and the Earth's Radiation Belts," *Science,* **144,** 292–94.

Little, C. G., and H. Leinbach. 1959. "The Riometer—A Device for the Continuous Measurement of Ionospheric Absorption," *Proc. I.R.E.,* **47,** 315–20.

McCracken, K. G. 1962. "The Cosmic-Ray Flare Effect, I, II, and III," *J. Geophys. Research,* **67,** 423–58.

McCracken, K. G., and R. A. R. Palmeira. 1960. "Comparison of Solar Cosmic Rays Injection Including July 17, 1959, and May 4, 1960," *J. Geophys. Research,* **65,** 2673–83.

McDiarmid, I. B., E. E. Budzinski, and D. C. Rose. 1964. "Energy Spectra and Angular Distributions of Electrons Associated with Auroral Events," Fifth International Space Science Symposium, Florence, Italy.

McDiarmid, I. B., and J. R. Burrows. 1964. "Diurnal Intensity Variations in the Outer Radiation Zone at 1000 km," *Can. J. Phys.,* **42,** 1135–48.

McDonald, F. B. 1959. "Primary Cosmic-Ray Intensity Near Solar Maximum," *Phys. Rev.,* **116,** 462–63.

McIlwain, C. E. 1959. "Results from Explorer IV," presented at NASA seminar on Van Allen Radiation, March 26–27 (unpublished).

McIlwain, C. E. 1960. "Direct Measurement of Particles Producing Visible Auroras," *J. Geophys. Research,* **65,** 2727–47.

McIlwain, C. E. 1961. "Coordinates for Mapping the Distribution of Geomagnetically Trapped Particles," *J. Geophys. Research,* **66,** 3681–92.

McIlwain, C. E. 1963. "The Radiation Belts, Natural and Artificial," *Science,* **142,** 355–61.

McIlwain, C. E. 1964. "Redistribution of Trapped Protons during a Magnetic Storm," Fifth International Space Science Symposium, Florence, Italy.

McIlwain, C. E., and G. Pizzella. 1963. "On the Energy Spectrum of Protons Trapped in the Earth's Inner Van Allen Zone," *J. Geophys. Research,* **68,** 1811–23.

McIlwain, C. E., R. W. Fillius, J. Valerio, and A. Dave. 1964. "Relay 1 Trapped Radiation Measurements," University of California at San Diego, Internal Report, unpublished.

Meyer, P., E. N. Parker, and J. A. Simpson. 1956. "Solar Cosmic Rays of February 1956 and Their Propagation Through Interplanetary Space," *Phys. Rev.,* **104,** 768–83.

Meyer, P., and R. Vogt. 1961. "Electrons in the Primary Cosmic Radiation," *Phys. Rev. Letters,* **6,** 193–96.

Meyer, P., and R. Vogt. 1962. "High Energy Electrons of Solar Origin," *Phys. Rev. Letters,* **8,** 387–89.

Naugle, J. E., and D. A. Kniffen. 1963. "Variations of the Proton Energy Spectrum with Position in the Inner Van Allen Belt," *J. Geophys. Research,* **68,** 4065–78.

Ney, E. P., and W. A. Stein. 1962. "Solar Protons, α-Particles, and Heavy Nuclei in Nov. 1960," *J. Geophys. Research,* **67,** 2087–2105.

Northrop, T. G. 1963. *The Adiabatic Motion of Charged Particles.* Interscience, New York.

O'Brien, B. J. 1963a. "A Large Diurnal Variation of the Geomagnetically Trapped Radiation," *J. Geophys. Research,* **68,** 989–95.

O'Brien, B. J. 1963b. "Review of Studies of Trapped Radiation with Satellite-Borne Apparatus," *Space Sci. Rev.,* **1,** 415–84.

O'Brien, B. J. 1964. "High-Latitude Geophysical Studies with Satellite Injun 3. 3. Precipitation of Electrons into the Atmosphere," *J. Geophys. Research,* **69,** 13–43.

O'Brien, B. J., and H. Taylor. 1964. "High-Latitude Geophysical Studies with Satellite Injun 3. 4. Auroras and Their Excitation," *J. Geophys. Research,* **69,** 45–63.

O'Brien, B. J., J. A. Van Allen, C. D. Laughlin, and L. A. Frank. 1962. "Absolute Electron Intensities in the Heart of the Outer Radiation Zone," *J. Geophys. Research,* **67,** 397–403.

Ohmholt, A. 1959. "Studies on the Excitation of Aurora Borealis. I. The Hydrogen Lines," *Geophys. Publikasjoner,* **20,** 1–40.

Parker, E. N., 1960. "Geomagnetic Fluctuations and the Form of the Outer Zone of the Van Allen Radiation Belt," *J. Geophys. Research,* **65,** 3117–30.

Parker, E. N. 1961a. "Effect of Hydromagnetic Waves in a Dipole Field on the Longitudinal Invariant," *J. Geophys. Research,* **66,** 693–708.

Parker, E. N. 1961b. "Sudden Expansion of the Corona Following a Large Solar Flare and the Attendant Magnetic Field and Cosmic Ray Effects," *Astrophys. J.,* **133,** 1014–33.

Peterson, L. E. 1964. "Positron-Electron Ratio of Precipitating Electrons," *J. Geophys. Research,* **69,** 3141–53.

Rosser, W. G. V., B. J. O'Brien, J. A. Van Allen, L. A. Frank, and C. D. Laughlin. 1962. "Electrons in the Earth's Outer Radiation Zone," *J. Geophys. Research,* **68,** 3131–48.

Rothwell, P., and C. E. McIlwain. 1959. "Satellite Observations of Solar Cosmic Rays," *Nature,* **184,** 138–40.

Sharp, R. D., J. E. Evans, R. G. Johnson, and J. B. Reagan. 1964. "Measurement of Total Energy Flux of Electrons Precipitating on Auroral Zones," Fifth International Space Science Symposium, Florence, Italy.

Singer, S. F. 1959. "Artificial Modification of the Earth's Radiation Belt," *Advances in the Astronautical Sciences* (Plenum Press, N.Y.), **4,** 335–54.

Stoffregen, W., and H. Derblom. 1962. "Auroral Hydrogen Emission Related to Charge Separation in the Magnetosphere," *Planet. Space Sci.,* **9,** 711–16.

Stone, E. C. 1963. "The Physical Significance and Application of L, B_0, and R_0 to Geomagnetically Trapped Particles," *J. Geophys. Research,* **68,** 4157–66.

Van Allen, J. A. 1959. "The Geomagnetically Trapped Corpuscular Radiation," *J. Geophys. Research,* **64,** 1683–89.

Van Allen, J. A., and L. A. Frank. 1959a. "Radiation Around the Earth to a Radial Distance of 107,400 km," *Nature,* **183,** 430–34.

Van Allen, J. A., and L. A. Frank. 1959b. "Radiation Measurements to 658,300 km with Pioneer IV," *Nature,* **184,** 219–24.

Van Allen, J. A., C. E. McIlwain, and G. H. Ludwig. 1959c. "Radiation Observations with Satellite 1958 ε," *J. Geophys. Research,* **64,** 271–86.

Vernov, S. N., and A. E. Chudakov. 1960. "Terrestrial Corpuscular and Cosmic Rays," in H. Kallmann Bijl, ed., *Space Research.* North-Holland Publishing Co., Amsterdam, pp. 751–96.

Vernov, S. N., A. E. Chudakov, and Yu. I. Logachev. 1959. "Study of Terrestrial Corpuscular Radiation and Cosmic Rays During the Flight of a Cosmic Rocket," *Soviet Phys. Doklady,* **4,** 154–57.

Walt, M., and W. M. MacDonald. 1964. "The Influence of the Earth's Atmosphere on Geomagnetically Trapped Particles," *Reviews of Geophysics,* **2,** in press.

Walt, M., L. F. Chase, Jr., J. B. Cladis, W. L. Imhof, and D. J. Knecht. 1960. "Energy Spectra and Altitude Dependence of Electrons Trapped in the Earth's Magnetic Field," in H. Kallmann Bijl, ed., *Space Research.* North-Holland Publishing Co., Amsterdam, pp. 910–20.

Webber, W. R. 1963. "An Evaluation of the Radiation Hazard Due to Solar-Particle Events," Boeing Company Report, No. D2-90469, December 1963.

Yoshida, S., G. H. Ludwig, and J. A. Van Allen. 1960. "Distribution of Trapped Radiation in the Geomagnetic Field," *J. Geophys. Research,* **65,** 807–13.

4. Solar Radiation

Francis S. Johnson

Southwest Center for Advanced Studies, Dallas

4. Solar Radiation

Francis S. Johnson

Southwest Center for Advanced Studies, Dallas

4.1. INTRODUCTION

Intense emission of light is the most obvious of all solar features. Visible radiation can be measured at the surface of the Earth. Since the Earth's atmosphere absorbs some of the radiation, it is necessary to make corrections for the atmospheric absorption in order to determine the intensity of the sunlight above the Earth's atmosphere. This correction cannot be made for all parts of the solar spectrum, however—there are several bands in the infrared portion of the spectrum to which the atmosphere is so opaque that none of the solar radiation within the band reaches the Earth's surface, and no measurement can be made. The infrared portion of the solar spectrum is quite regular and smooth, however, and it is possible to interpolate between adjoining spectral regions where measurements can be made. In this way, measurements have been made of the solar spectrum well into the infrared, to wavelengths as long as about 15 microns (μ). Because the wavelengths in different parts of the spectrum are designated in different units, we are stating here these units and their relationships: $1\ \mu = 10^{-4}$ cm; $1\ A = 10^{-8}$ cm.

At the short-wavelength end of the solar spectrum, the situation is different; ozone in the Earth's atmosphere, mainly at altitudes near 20 or 30 km, is so opaque to ultraviolet radiation with wavelengths shorter than about 0.3 μ that the solar spectrum observed on Earth is effectively terminated at that wavelength. It would not be possible to say much about this spectral region if it were not for rocket observations made above the atmospheric ozone. At wavelengths shorter than about 0.2 μ, other atmospheric constituents are also opaque, and it is necessary to make observations at correspondingly higher altitudes, which rockets can also conveniently reach. In recent years observations have been extended over the entire ultraviolet spectrum down into the X-ray region, although the quantitative values are still tentative and the variation through the solar cycle has not been determined.

4.2. SOLAR-IRRADIANCE DATA

The bulk of the energy in the solar spectrum lies between wavelengths 0.3 and 4.0 μ, with approximately one per cent of the energy lying beyond each of these limits. This portion of the solar spectrum has been studied at the Earth's surface, with corrections made for atmospheric absorption to obtain the spectral intensity of solar radiation outside the Earth's atmosphere. The distribution of energy in the solar radiation incident on the Earth's upper atmosphere is shown in **Fig. 4–1**. Values of the spectral irradiance (i.e., the incident energy flux per unit area per unit wavelength) are given in Table 4-1; these values, which apply when the Earth is at its mean distance from the sun, are based upon a study of the solar constant by Johnson (1954), modified below 2600 A according to more recent rocket ultraviolet data obtained by Detwiler *et al.* (1961). The solar constant is the total solar irradiance at the Earth's mean distance from the sun; it is equal to the area under the curve shown in **Fig. 4-1** (extended to longer wavelengths), and it has the value 0.140 w/cm². The visible and infrared (the ultraviolet not included) portion of the solar spectrum is well approximated in spectral quality by the radiation from a 6000 °K blackbody, whereas the total amount of electromagnetic radiation emitted by the sun is the same as that from a 5800 °K blackbody.

The solar spectrum below 0.3 μ must be obtained from rocket observations, since virtually none of the solar radiation in this spectral region is able to pene-

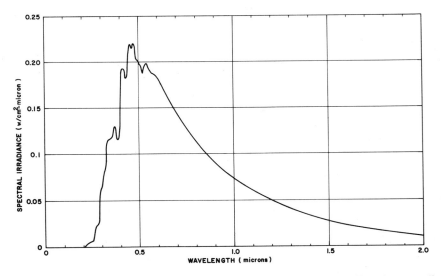

Fig. 4-1. Solar spectral irradiance above the Earth's atmosphere at the Earth's mean distance from the sun.

TABLE 4-1

SOLAR-SPECTRAL-IRRADIANCE DATA—0.22 TO 7.0 MICRONS

λ^a (μ)	H_λ (w/cm²μ)	P_λ (%)	λ (μ)	H_λ (w/cm²μ)	P_λ (%)	λ (μ)	H_λ (w/cm²μ)	P_λ (%)	λ (μ)	H_λ (w/cm²μ)	P_λ (%)
0.22	0.0062	0.06	0.395	0.120	8.60	0.57	0.187	33.2	1.9	0.01274	93.02
0.225	0.0070	0.08	0.40	0.154	9.08	0.575	0.187	33.9	2.0	0.01079	93.87
0.23	0.0072	0.11	0.405	0.188	9.70	0.58	0.187	34.5	2.1	0.00917	94.58
0.235	0.0064	0.14	0.41	0.194	10.3	0.585	0.185	35.2	2.2	0.00785	95.20
0.24	0.0068	0.16	0.415	0.192	11.0	0.59	0.184	35.9	2.3	0.00676	95.71
0.245	0.0078	0.18	0.42	0.192	11.7	0.595	0.183	36.5	2.4	0.00585	96.18
0.25	0.0076	0.21	0.425	0.189	12.4	0.60	0.181	37.2	2.5	0.00509	96.57
0.255	0.0112	0.25	0.43	0.178	13.0	0.61	0.177	38.4	2.6	0.00445	96.90
0.26	0.014	0.29	0.435	0.182	13.7	0.62	0.174	39.7	2.7	0.00390	97.21
0.265	0.020	0.35	0.44	0.203	14.4	0.63	0.170	40.9	2.8	0.00343	97.47
0.27	0.025	0.42	0.445	0.215	15.1	0.64	0.166	42.1	2.9	0.00303	97.72
0.275	0.022	0.51	0.45	0.220	15.9	0.65	0.162	43.3	3.0	0.00268	97.90
0.28	0.024	0.59	0.455	0.219	16.7	0.66	0.159	44.5	3.1	0.00230	98.08
0.285	0.034	0.70	0.46	0.216	17.5	0.67	0.155	45.6	3.2	0.00214	98.24
0.29	0.052	0.85	0.465	0.215	18.2	0.68	0.151	46.7	3.3	0.00191	98.39
0.295	0.063	1.06	0.47	0.217	19.0	0.69	0.148	47.8	3.4	0.00171	98.52
0.30	0.061	1.30	0.475	0.220	19.8	0.70	0.144	48.8	3.5	0.00153	98.63
0.305	0.067	1.50	0.48	0.216	20.6	0.71	0.141	49.8	3.6	0.00139	98.74
0.31	0.076	1.66	0.485	0.203	21.3	0.72	0.137	50.8	3.7	0.00125	98.83
0.315	0.082	2.03	0.49	0.199	22.0	0.73	0.134	51.8	3.8	0.00114	98.91
0.32	0.085	2.32	0.495	0.204	22.8	0.74	0.130	52.7	3.9	0.00103	98.99
0.325	0.102	2.66	0.50	0.198	23.5	0.75	0.127	53.7	4.0	0.00095	99.05
0.33	0.115	3.08	0.505	0.197	24.2	0.80	0.1127	57.9	4.1	0.00087	99.13
0.335	0.111	3.46	0.51	0.196	24.9	0.85	0.1003	61.7	4.2	0.00080	99.18
0.34	0.111	3.86	0.515	0.189	25.6	0.90	0.895	65.1	4.3	0.00073	99.23
0.345	0.117	4.27	0.52	0.187	26.3	0.95	0.0803	68.1	4.4	0.00067	99.29
0.35	0.118	4.69	0.525	0.192	26.9	1.0	0.0725	70.9	4.5	0.00061	99.33
0.355	0.116	5.10	0.53	0.195	27.6	1.1	0.0606	75.7	4.6	0.00056	99.38
0.36	0.116	5.53	0.535	0.197	28.3	1.2	0.0501	79.6	4.7	0.00051	99.41
0.365	0.129	5.95	0.54	0.198	29.0	1.3	0.0406	82.9	4.8	0.00048	99.45
0.37	0.133	6.42	0.545	0.198	29.8	1.4	0.0328	85.5	4.9	0.00044	99.48
0.375	0.132	6.90	0.55	0.195	30.5	1.5	0.0267	87.6	5.0	0.00042	99.51
0.38	0.123	7.35	0.555	0.192	31.2	1.6	0.0220	89.4	6.0	0.00021	99.74
0.385	0.115	7.78	0.56	0.190	31.8	1.7	0.0182	90.83	7.0	0.00012	99.86
0.39	0.112	8.19	0.565	0.189	32.5	1.8	0.0152	92.03			

^{a} λ is wavelength; H_λ is spectral irradiance; and P_λ is the percentage of the solar constant associated with wavelengths shorter than λ.

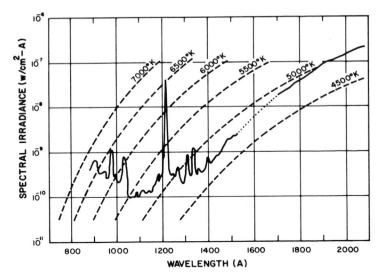

Fig. 4-2. Solar ultraviolet spectral irradiance above the Earth's atmosphere observed with a photographic spectrograph by the U. S. Naval Research Laboratory.

trate the atmosphere and reach the Earth's surface. An example of a solar spectrum for the 850 to 2100 A region obtained with a photographic rocket spectrograph is shown in **Fig. 4-2** (Detwiler *et al.*, 1961). Shown for comparison are spectral irradiance curves for blackbody radiation at temperatures ranging from 4500 to 7000 °K, the physical dimensions chosen for the blackbody being the same as those of the sun. Data on the solar spectral irradiance down to 850 A, according to Detwiler, *et al.* (1961), are given in Table 4-2.

In addition to continuum radiation, there are a number of emission lines that show up in the solar spectrum, especially below 1900 A; these contribute only a small amount of energy compared to the continuum at all wavelengths longer than 850 A, except in the region of the atomic-hydrogen Lyman-alpha line. At shorter wavelengths also, it appears probable that there is a background of continuum radiation that contains more energy than all but the few strongest emission lines. A list of the stronger lines that have been observed and their intensities are given in Table 4-3 (Detwiler *et al.*, 1961; Hall *et al.*, 1963; Kreplin, 1961). The irradiances given in Table 4-2 include the contributions from any emission lines that fall within a 50 A interval centered on the indicated wavelength.

The solar spectrum below 1000 A is shown in **Fig. 4-3**, based on photoelectric measurements made by Hinteregger *et al.* (1964); the spectrum is shown in the form of a block diagram indicating the average spectral irradiance over

TABLE 4-2

SOLAR-SPECTRAL-IRRADIANCE DATA—850 TO 2200 A

λ^a (A)	H_λ (w/cm²·A)	P_λ (per cent)
850	2.2×10^{-10}	1.3×10^{-4}
900	5.0×10^{-10}	1.4×10^{-4}
950	3.0×10^{-10}	1.5×10^{-4}
1000	3.6×10^{-10}	1.7×10^{-4}
1050	2.0×10^{-10}	1.8×10^{-4}
1100	1.2×10^{-10}	1.8×10^{-4}
1150	1.6×10^{-10}	1.9×10^{-4}
1200	114×10^{-10}	2.0×10^{-4}
1250	3.0×10^{-10}	6.0×10^{-4}
1300	3.6×10^{-10}	6.2×10^{-4}
1350	5.2×10^{-10}	6.3×10^{-4}
1400	5.2×10^{-10}	6.4×10^{-4}
1450	1.0×10^{-9}	6.7×10^{-4}
1500	1.9×10^{-9}	7×10^{-4}
1550	3.4×10^{-9}	8×10^{-4}
1600	6.4×10^{-9}	1.0×10^{-3}
1650	1.0×10^{-8}	1.2×10^{-3}
1700	1.64×10^{-8}	1.8×10^{-3}
1750	2.4×10^{-8}	2.1×10^{-3}
1800	3.8×10^{-8}	3.2×10^{-3}
1850	5.6×10^{-8}	4.9×10^{-3}
1900	8.2×10^{-8}	7.0×10^{-3}
1950	1.1×10^{-7}	1.1×10^{-2}
2000	1.4×10^{-7}	1.5×10^{-2}
2050	1.8×10^{-7}	2.0×10^{-2}
2100	2.9×10^{-7}	3×10^{-2}
2150	4.8×10^{-7}	4×10^{-2}
2200	6.2×10^{-7}	6×10^{-2}

[a] λ is wavelength; H_λ is spectral irradiance; and P_λ is the percentage of the solar constant associated with wavelengths shorter than λ.

given wavelength intervals, ignoring a few of the more prominent spectral emission lines, and these lines are shown superimposed upon the block diagram. Hinteregger's observed intensities have been corrected for atmospheric absorption above the observing altitude of about 200 km to obtain the values shown. The intensities near 1000 A, shown in **Fig. 4-3**, agree fairly well with the values shown in **Fig. 4-2**, and detailed spectral features in regions of overlap generally

TABLE 4-3

Solar-Ultraviolet-Spectral-Line Intensities

Source	λ (A)	Intensity (10^{-8} w/cm²)	Source	λ (A)	Intensity (10^{-8} w/cm²)
Si III	1892.03	1.0	N III	991.58	0.10
Si II[a]	1817.42	4.5	N III[a]	989.79	0.06
Si II	1808.01	1.5	C III	977.03	0.50
Al II	1670.81	0.8	H I(δ)	949.74	0.10
C I[a]	1657.00	1.6	H I(ε)	937.80	0.05
He II	1640.47	0.7	H I(Cont.)	911–840	2.3
C I	1561.40	0.9	O II, III[a]	835	0.13
C IV	1550.77	0.6	O IV[a]	790.2	0.03
C IV	1548.19	1.1	O IV	787.7	0.08
Si II	1533.44	0.41	Ne VIII	780.3	0.04
Si II	1526.70	0.38	Ne VIII	770.4	0.11
Si IV	1402.73	0.13	N IV	765.1	0.06
Si IV	1393.73	0.30	O III[a]	703	0.07
C II	1335.68	0.50	O V	629.7	0.56
C II	1334.51	0.50	Mg X	625	0.13
O I	1306.02	0.25	Mg X	610	0.26
O I	1304.86	0.20	He I	584.3	0.54
O I	1302.17	0.13	O IV[a]	555–553	0.19
Si II	1265.04	0.20	He I	537	0.05
Si II[a]	1260.66	0.10	Si XII	499	0.17
N V[a]	1242.78	0.03	Ne VII	465.2	0.12
N V	1238.80	0.04	Mg IX	368.1	0.32
H I(α)	1215.67	51.0[b]	He II(α)	303.8	2.5
Si III	1206.52	0.30	Fe XV	283	0.43
C III[a]	1175.70	0.10	He II	256	0.23
C I[a]	1139.89	0.03	<200A		10
N II[a]	1085.70	0.06	<20A		0.23
O VI	1037.61	0.25	<8A		0.02
O VI	1031.91	0.20			
H I(β)	1025.72	0.60			

[a] Blended with additional lines.   [b] Within 1 A bandwidth centered on line.

agree within about 30 per cent; occasionally poorer agreements occur with some spectral lines, perhaps reflecting a facet of solar activity. The spectral lines shown in **Fig. 4-3** are presented with an effective line width of 10 A. Since their true widths are much less than this, their peak intensities are higher than the ones shown in the figure.

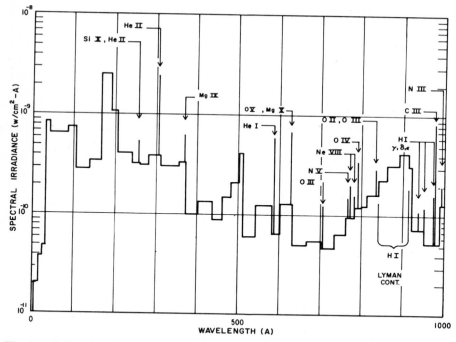

Fig. 4-3. Solar ultraviolet spectral irradiance above the Earth's atmosphere, derived from measurements by Hinteregger *et al.* (1964). The lines are shown as if they had an effective line width of 10 A.

4.3. THE SOLAR WIND

Although it is not intended that particle radiation from the sun be discussed here, the presence of a continuous outflow of particles from the sun with energies of the order of a kilovolt is probably worth mentioning. This flux of particles is generally referred to as the solar wind (Parker, 1958). It results from a continuous hydrodynamical expansion of the solar corona. Its presence was first recognized on the basis of indirect evidence—the deflection of certain types of comet tails away from the sun, and geomagnetic effects. The indirect evidence was confirmed by observations made in the Mariner 2 spacecraft, which observed about 5 protons/cm³ in interplanetary space near the Earth's orbit moving away from the sun with a velocity of about 500 km/sec under quiet solar conditions (Snyder *et al.*, 1963). Under disturbed solar conditions, the concentrations may rise to 10^2 protons/cm³ or higher and the velocities to 1500 km/sec (10 kev). The enhanced fluxes under disturbed solar conditions give rise to magnetic storms and auroras, but the detailed mechanisms involved are not understood.

4.4. SOLAR VARIATIONS

Depending upon one's viewpoint, the sun may appear to be characterized by either extreme constancy or extreme variability. It is an exceedingly stable source of radiation in the visible and adjoining spectral regions. Any changes that occur in the solar constant are so small that their existence is difficult to establish. However, even in the visible emissions, it is clear that the sun is variable in some degree, as indicated by the appearance of dark spots on the sun, the sunspots. Other indications of variable solar conditions are the prominences that can be seen at the edge of the solar disk with special observing equipment and the structure that can be seen on the surface of the sun when viewed through filters that pass only the light from certain atoms, such as hydrogen alpha (Balmer alpha) or calcium K radiation. Solar flares can be observed by means of such techniques.

The most useful index of solar activity is probably the sunspot number, which exhibits a strong 11-year variation. The sunspot number is obtained by means of an equation involving the number of sunspot groups and the number of iden-

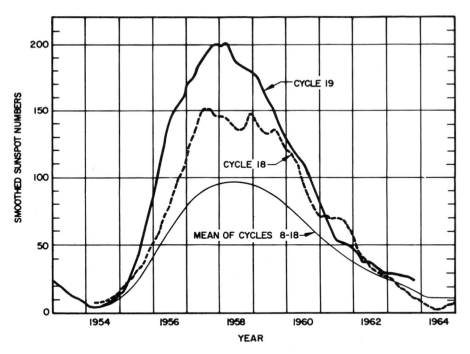

Fig. 4-4. Variation in sunspot number through the solar cycle. Cycle 18 and the mean of cycles 8 through 18 are shown for comparison, displaced in time to agree in phase with cycle 19. Cycles 18 and 19 were both much more intense than the average of cycles 8 through 18.

tifiable spots. **Figure 4-4** shows the variation in the sunspot number (monthly-average values) during the period since the commencement of the present cycle, number 19, in April 1954 (Virginia Lincoln, National Bureau of Standards, private communication). The previous cycle, number 18 (displaced in time to agree with the present cycle), and the average of cycles 8 to 18 are also shown. During the sunspot maximum, solar flares occur with increased frequency. Some of these generate soft cosmic radiation (see **Fig. 3-17**), and many of them emit radio noise (see Section 6.5).

The continuum radiation probably does not change perceptibly during the progress of a sunspot cycle, even in the ultraviolet. However, the line radiations probably exhibit a variation, and, in general, such variations become relatively more important at the shorter wavelengths, especially in the X-ray region. Kreplin (1961) indicates that, near sunspot-cycle minimum, the X-ray spectrum below 200 A is lower than at sunspot-cycle maximum by a factor of about 7; below 20 A, the factor is 60, and below 8 A, about 600.

The X-ray intensities also vary from day to day, increasing for short periods of time when flares occur. On August 24, 1959, 11 minutes after a class 2+ flare attained peak optical intensity, the X-ray spectrum above 20 A showed an increase by a factor of 3 over the value prevailing just before the flare; the 8 to 20 A band increased by a factor of 7; and the 2 to 8 A band increased by a factor of 26. On August 31, 1959, four minutes after a class 2+ flare reached its maximum phase, the X-ray spectrum above 20 A increased by a factor of 12; the 8 to 20 A band increased by a factor of over 20; and the 2 to 8 A band by a factor of over 100. The greater relative (but not absolute) increase in the 2 to 8 A band than in the 8 to 20 A band indicates a very important hardening of the X-ray spectrum. These data are summarized in Table 4-4. Also included is an observation during a bright surge prominence of Class 3 on July 24, 1959; this event also produced a hardening of the X-ray spectrum but not much increase in total flux.

During solar flares, the shortest observed wavelength is usually about 1 A, although shorter wavelengths probably occur for a few minutes at the beginning of the flare. On a few occasions, very short-wavelength emissions have been observed. Chubb *et al.* (1960) have reported X-ray wavelengths as short as 0.15 A (energies as high as 80 kev). Kreplin (1961) has reported measurements with scintillator detectors showing X-rays with energies as great as 125 kev during a Class 2+ solar flare. The incident flux with energies greater than 20 kev (<0.6 A) was about 4.5×10^{-13} w/cm².

Satellite experiments have provided many useful data on X-rays in the 2 to 8 A band over the time interval from July to November, 1960 (Kreplin *et al.*, 1962). The normally incident flux in this period was less than 0.006×10^{-8}

TABLE 4-4

INTENSITIES OF SOLAR X-RAYS, 10^{-8} w/cm²

	2–8 A	8–20 A	20–200 A
Sunspot min (quiet sun)	0.00003	0.004	1.3
Sunspot max (quiet sun)	0.02	0.23	10
Class 3 bright surge prominence 7-24-59	0.13	0.89	8
Class 2+ flare 8-24-59	0.26	1.6	21
Class 2+ flare 8-31-59	>2.20	>4.5	92

w/cm², which was the approximate threshold of the detector. Increases above this level were seen with a variety of solar events—flares, active prominence regions, bright surges on the limb, and certain limb flares. Significant changes were seen to occur in time periods as short as one minute. Whenever the flux rose above 0.02×10^{-8} w/cm², ionospheric effects of the radiation were observed. The Lyman-alpha line of hydrogen was also monitored; if its level of intensity changed at all with the X-ray variations, it was by no more than 18 per cent. However, the Lyman-alpha observations were limited to the early part of the flight, July 13 to August 3.

REFERENCES

Chubb, T. A., H. Friedman, and R. W. Kreplin. 1960. "Measurements Made of High-Energy X-Rays Accompanying Three Class 2+ Solar Flares," *J. Geophys. Research,* **65,** 1831–32.

Detwiler, C. R., D. L. Garrett, J. D. Purcell, and R. Tousey. 1961. "The Intensity Distribution in the Ultraviolet Solar Spectrum," *Ann. Geophys.,* **17,** 263–72.

Hall, L. A., K. R. Damon, and H. E. Hinteregger. 1963. "Solar Extreme Ultraviolet Photon Flux Measurements in the Upper Atmosphere of August 1961," in W. Priester, ed., *Space Research III.* North-Holland Publishing Co., Amsterdam, pp. 745–59.

Hinteregger, H. E., L. A. Hall, and G. Schmedtke. 1964. "Solar XUV Radiation and Neutral Particles Distribution in July 1963 Thermosphere," Fifth International Space Science Symposium, Florence, Italy.

Johnson, F. S. 1954. "The Solar Constant," *J. Meteorol.,* **11,** 431–39.

Kreplin, R. W. 1961. "Solar X-Rays," *Ann. Geophys.,* **17,** 151–61.

Kreplin, R. W., T. A. Chubb, and H. Friedman. 1962. "X-Ray and Lyman-Alpha Emission from the Sun as Measured from the NRL SR-1 Satellite," *J. Geophys. Research,* **67,** 2231–53.

Parker, E. N. 1958. "Interaction of the Solar Wind with the Geomagnetic Field," *Phys. Fluids,* **1,** 171–87.

Snyder, C. W., M. Neugebauer, and U. R. Rao. 1963. "The Solar Wind Velocity and Its Correlation with Cosmic-Ray Variations and with Solar and Geomagnetic Activity," *J. Geophys. Research,* **68,** 6361–70.

5. Micrometeoroids

James F. Vedder

National Aeronautics and Space Administration,
Ames Research Center, Moffett Field, California

5. Micrometeoroids

James F. Vedder

National Aeronautics and Space Administration,
Ames Research Center, Moffett Field, California

5.1. INTRODUCTION

Meteoroids are astronomical bodies which travel in generally large and frequently highly eccentric orbits about the sun. If they strike the Earth's atmosphere, the observable effect produced is known as a meteor. The particle is known as a meteorite if it reaches the Earth's surface. Although a few meteoroids are large and weigh many tons, most of them are small. Meteors that can be seen with the naked eye during a few minutes' observation of the night sky are caused by meteoroids which are about the size of peas or occasionally even as large as golf balls. Smaller meteoroids may produce meteors which can be observed by reflection of radio waves. Meteoroids that are too small to produce either visual or radar meteors are called micrometeoroids, and their diameters are less than 1 mm.

The existence of dust in interplanetary space has been well established. The dust particles, which range in size down to dimensions of less than a micron ($1\mu = 10^{-4}$ cm), consist mainly of micrometeoroids. Beyond the protective atmosphere of the Earth, meteoroids present a possible hazard to space vehicles. The size, mass, spatial distribution, velocities, and number densities of the particles are not well known; however, the data presented in this chapter are considered to be the most reliable estimates presently available.

5.2. ENVIRONMENTAL EFFECTS ON MICROMETEOROIDS

Primarily, the micrometeoroid motions are governed by the law of gravitation. In the two-body problem with mass M much greater than mass m, the orbit of m about M will be hyperbolic, parabolic, or elliptic depending upon whether the sum of the kinetic energy of the small body and its gravitational potential energy (taken to be zero for infinite separation) is respectively greater than, equal to, or less than zero. For elliptic orbits, which are the main concern in studying meteoroids, the total energy depends only on a, the semi-major axis. The orbital velocity is

$$v = \left[GM \left(\frac{2}{r} - \frac{1}{a} \right) \right]^{1/2}, \tag{5-1}$$

where G is the gravitational constant (6.670×10^{-8} dyne-cm^2/g^2) and r is the distance between the centers of the two masses M and m. For a micrometeoroid in a closed heliocentric orbit and approaching the Earth, the geocentric velocity v_R at a distance R from the center of the Earth may be calculated from

$$v_R^2 = v_d^2 + \frac{2GM_e}{R}, \tag{5-2}$$

where M_e is the mass of the Earth and v_d is the vector difference of the heliocentric velocities of the Earth and the particle at a distance of separation where the gravitational potential energy with respect to the Earth is negligible. From Eqs. 5-1 and 5-2, one can calculate the expected velocity range of particles arriving at the Earth for particles trapped within the solar system. The maximum velocity occurs for a head-on collision with a meteoroid at perihelion in a retrograde parabolic orbit; addition of the Earth's orbital velocity of 30 km/sec and the meteoroid's velocity of 42 km/sec gives a relative v_d of 72 km/sec. The velocity increment from the Earth's gravitational attraction increases this to 73 km/sec for the maximum geocentric velocity just above the atmosphere for meteoroids that are members of the solar system. The minimum velocity occurs for a meteoroid in a direct circular orbit at one astronomical unit (1 A.U. is the Earth's mean distance from the sun); then $v_d = 0$, and the final velocity just above the atmosphere is the free-fall velocity of 11 km/sec. If the objects were in orbit about the Earth, the velocities could be as low as 8 km/sec near the Earth and even less farther out. For meteoroids of galactic origin, the maximum velocity would be greater than the parabolic limit, which varies from 73 km/sec for head-on collisions to 16 km/sec for rear-end collisions. For interactions with space vehicles, the velocities relative to the spacecraft should be considered rather than the geocentric velocities mentioned above.

In addition to the gravitational force of attraction, several other phenomena influence the behavior of micrometeoroids in space. On sufficiently small particles, solar electromagnetic-radiation pressure exerts a repulsive force that exceeds the attractive force of gravitation and sweeps the particles from the solar system. For perfectly absorbing spheres in radiative equilibrium, Robertson (1937) calculates a minimum radius of $0.6/\rho$ micron (where ρ is the density in g/cm^3) for particles remaining in interplanetary space without being blown out of the solar system by radiation pressure. For small particles released from larger orbiting bodies, it is not the cancellation of the two forces that determines the minimum size; rather, it is the condition that the total energy be greater than zero (Harwit, 1963). For nearly parabolic orbits, even 1-mm-diameter particles may be removed within one period. In Halley's comet, the 2 per cent reduction in gravitational force due to radiation pressure on 30-μ-diameter grains is enough to eliminate them. For a circular parent orbit, the minimum diameter for remaining in the solar system is about 2.5 μ, corresponding to a 50 per cent reduction of the attractive force; on the other hand, this size can exist in a circular orbit if the velocity is 0.7 times the unperturbed orbital velocity. If the particle sizes are less than the wavelength of light, the radiation interaction is different, and in some cases the particles may not be blown away.

The Poynting-Robertson effect (Robertson, 1937; Wyatt and Whipple, 1950), which is a retardation of the orbital motion of particles by the relativistic aberration of the repulsive force of the impinging solar radiation, causes the dust to spiral into the sun in times much shorter than the age of the Earth. The radial velocity varies inversely as the particle size—a 1000-μ-diameter particle near the orbit of Mars would reach the sun in about 60 million years. Whipple (1955) extends the effects to include the solar corpuscular radiation pressure, which increases both the minimum particle size and the drag. Further, the corpuscular radiation, i.e., the solar wind protons, must sputter away the surface atoms of the dust and cause a slow diminution in size, with a resultant increase in both the Poynting-Robertson effect and the ratio of the repulsive force to the gravitational force. On the basis of laboratory experiments, the estimated rate of material loss by solar wind sputtering at 1 A.U. is about 0.4×10^{-8} cm/yr for iron and stony materials (Wehner et al., 1963a). Thus a micron-size grain at 1 A.U. would vanish in 2.5×10^4 years by this mechanism. Since the erosion rate depends on the solar wind flux, an inverse-square dependence on the distance from the sun is expected. On the other hand, there are mechanisms that may reduce or even reverse the Poynting-Robertson effect: spin increases or decreases the drag on a particle, depending on the direction of the spin (Jacchia, 1963); the rotation of the solar wind corpuscles about the sun also produces an effect (Singer, 1962). Of course the shape, composition, and orientation of the micrometeoroids can have a large effect on the magnitudes of the various forces.

The Poynting-Robertson effect causes the semi-major axis of orbits to diminish more rapidly than the semi-minor axis, with a consequent tendency toward circular orbits as the particles move toward the sun. Also, planetary gravitational attraction increases the dust concentration near the plane of the ecliptic as the sun is approached. At one astronomical unit from the sun, the dust orbits are probably nearly circular. If such is the case, the particles within a distance of about 4×10^6 km of the Earth will have, relative to the Earth, a kinetic energy less than their potential energy, and they will be captured into temporary orbits about the Earth.

A number of authors (deJager, 1955; Beard, 1961; Singer, 1961; Ruskol, 1963; Moroz, 1963; Dole, 1962; Southworth, 1963; and others) have considered the problem of planetary concentration of interplanetary dust. Various schemes are proposed for trapping the particles into Earth orbits that eventually enter the Earth's atmosphere. Such processes as gravitational enhancement, radiation pressure, gas and charge drag with rupture of frangible materials, interparticle collisions, and the like are discussed. The estimates of the increase in flux near the Earth over that in interplanetary space vary between one and five orders of magnitude. It is also quite probable that the moon is a heavy contributor (Whipple, 1961) to any dust blanket near the Earth, owing to the escape of ejecta from meteoroid impacts on the moon; trajectory calculations (Varsavsky, 1958) lend further credence to this hypothesis. Even the various conjectured, high-porosity lunar surfaces (Hibbs, 1963; Hapke and Van Horn, 1963) would yield substantial amounts of ejecta exceeding escape velocity, as demonstrated in impact studies on such materials (Gault et al., 1963a). Incidentally, near the moon the ejecta with less-than-escape velocity should produce a heavy particle flux (Gault et al., 1963b).

Since there is a continual loss of micrometeoric material in space because of the radiation effects, there must be a continual replenishment; otherwise, micrometeoroids would have disappeared from interplanetary space. There are several possible sources. According to Whipple (1955), cometary debris is sufficient to replenish the material spiraling into the sun, maintaining a fairly steady state. Asteroidal collisions are also thought to contribute material. Harwit (1963) questions the ability of comets to maintain the influx to the sun unless the Poynting-Robertson effect is inhibited in some way. He also believes that an asteroidal origin would produce highly variable fluxes, in which case we now are in a period of high activity. As another source, intergalactic dust may be captured (Best and Patterson, 1962) by means of gravitational accretion coupled with the Poynting-Robertson effect and may provide up to one-third the amount that Whipple (1955) requires to maintain the zodiacal cloud.

There has been much conjecture as to the form of the micrometeoroids. Are they solid, porous, or whiskerlike objects, or are all these present in space? The whisker forms, single or matted filaments, are considered to be logical structures for primordial material as well as for material recondensed from the vapor state resulting from impacts and sputtering (Donn and Sears, 1963; Hibbs, 1963). Whipple's (1950) icy comet model sublimes near perihelion to leave loosely bound conglomerates of solid particles that may disperse from the parent body. Studies of sputtering on materials (Wehner et al., 1963b) indicate development of porous, brittle, and fibrous crusts on surfaces under very long exposure to solar corpuscular bombardment.

5.3. DIRECT MEASUREMENTS ON MICROMETEORIC FLUX

One cannot make a very satisfactory guess about the micrometeoric flux in space. Even in the neighborhood of the Earth, where information has been obtained both directly and indirectly, the derived flux values vary by at least four orders of magnitude. This large discrepancy demonstrates the inadequacies of the experimental methods and the lack of understanding of the various phenomena involved. Beyond a few million kilometers from the Earth, but still in the region of the Earth's orbit, a prediction of the flux of dust is even more unreliable. At greater distances from the sun, the situation is still less certain.

There are several sources of evidence on the micrometeoric environment. Direct information has been obtained from rockets and satellites equipped with impact sensors. In addition, the size distribution obtained from visual and radar observations of meteors may be extrapolated to the micrometeoric domain. From the brightness of the F component of the solar corona and the brightness of the zodiacal light, an estimate of the particle sizes, concentrations, and spatial distribution can be derived for regions of space near the ecliptic plane. Another important source of evidence only recently receiving much attention is the analysis of atmospheric dust for a meteoric component. The cores of deep-sea sediments and content of collectors in remote regions are valuable in this category. The data provide a measure of the total mass of cosmic material incident upon the Earth.

The direct evidence on the micrometeoric environment near the Earth is obtained primarily from piezoelectric sensors (essentially microphones) installed on rockets, satellites, and space probes. Most of the data fall within an order of magnitude of the relationship (McCracken *et al.*, 1961 ; Dubin and McCracken, 1962),

$$\log I = -17.0 - 1.70 \log m , \qquad (5\text{-}3)$$

where I is the average number of impacts/m^2-sec by particles of mass greater than or equal to m grams. Assuming that the microphones are momentum-sensitive, one derives a mass from an assumed mean velocity, usually about 30 km/sec. The equation is valid near Earth in the mass range 10^{-10} g $\leqq m \leqq 10^{-6}$ g ; it is marked "McCracken" in **Fig. 5-1**. Sounding rocket data from different types of detectors indicate that the curve flattens out toward smaller masses, as might be expected from radiation pressure effects. The data show daily and diurnal variations, and the actual rate may vary by an order of magnitude in a

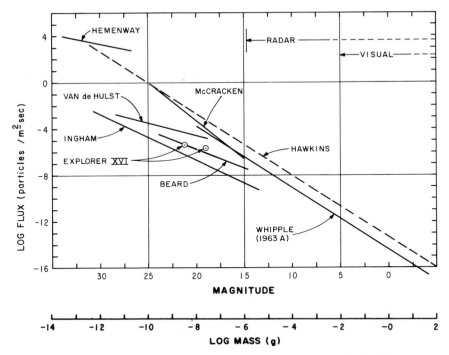

Fig. 5-1. Cumulative micrometeoric flux versus mass and visual magnitude. The curves, except for the zodiacal light derivations, include a 50 per cent shielding factor for the Earth. The magnitude scale is based on a 1 g, 30-km/sec meteoroid producing a meteor of zero visual magnitude.

short time. This behavior seems contrary to that expected from the regularizing action of the Poynting-Robertson effect. In addition, Harwit's arguments mentioned earlier favor a short stream lifetime for these small sizes. Possibly the fluctuations can be explained by recent disintegrations of larger, frangible meteoroids and cometary material during their perihelion passage.

Space probes have yielded some information. Pioneer 1 recorded a decrease in flux with distance from the Earth on the basis of only a few counts. Also, the second and third Russian space probes indicate a much lower impact rate away from the Earth (Nazarova, 1963). The Mariner 2 flight to Venus registered one definite impact (Alexander, 1962). Individually, these results being based on very few events would be of dubious validity, but as a whole they seem to indicate that the flux is several orders of magnitude less at great distances from the Earth. Several workers (Whipple, 1961; Hibbs, 1961; Nazarova, 1963) have concluded from analyses of such data that there is a decrease in particle flux with distance from the Earth. Whipple, for example, fits the data with an inverse 1.4

power of the altitude to about 5×10^5 km. This relationship gives a difference of five orders of magnitude in fluxes at the top of the atmosphere and in interplanetary space. However, Dubin and McCracken (1962) point out that the data must be normalized on the basis of the actual flux-mass distribution before one can derive an altitude dependence. The available data are insufficient to resolve the problem. The large fluctuations indicate that direct accretion is more likely than long-life Earth orbits. The latter case should also show a flatter influx curve, since the smaller particles would be removed more rapidly by various drag effects.

The calibration of piezoelectric sensors in terms of the particle parameters is very uncertain. Many workers believe that the response is proportional to the incident momentum of the particles, a relation deduced from laboratory results linearly extrapolated to meteoric velocities. However, one must expect that vaporization and ejection of material by hypervelocity impacts would cause a deviation from a linear relationship. In the United States, most of the sensors are calibrated by dropping small spheres on their sensitive surfaces. The Russian experimenters claim that only a small fraction of the impulse from the sensors is caused by the incident momentum, with the remainder being momentum of ejected material from the sensor, the ejection momentum being linearly related to the particle energy. Hypervelocity impact calibration is being done at the threshold of meteoric velocities, but there are no good methods for higher velocities. There may be an order-of-magnitude uncertainty in the calibration extrapolation. The threshold mass is derived from the momentum threshold with the assumption of a mean impact velocity, usually about 30 km/sec. A typical threshold mass of about 10^{-9} g corresponds to a 10-μ-diameter sphere of density 2 g/cm³. However, the conversion from mass to size is unreliable, since many photographic meteors give evidence of a fluffy, loosely bound meteoric structure with densities as low as 0.01 g/cm³. To what extent such low density applies to micrometeoroids is unknown. The velocity value used is also open to some question; if a substantial fraction of the dust is orbiting about the Earth, only about one-third of the above-mentioned average velocity should be used in deriving the mass. The diurnal and altitude variation in the observed flux may be partly due to the dependence of the detector sensitivity on the incident velocity.

A sounding rocket experiment (Hemenway and Soberman, 1962) has contributed some interesting information by collecting material between 88- and 168-km altitude. The particles were mainly of sub-micron dimensions, and they apparently had quite low velocities. They were typed as dense spheres, irregular particles, or fluffy particles. The flux-versus-mass curve is quite flat and unexpectedly high, as shown in **Fig. 5-1**. The results might possibly be explained by breakup of meteoroids in the outer fringes of the Earth's atmosphere. The particle forms may provide insight into the structure of the actual debris in space.

The first direct information on meteoroid penetration rate has been obtained from the Explorer 16 satellite (Hastings, 1963), devoted exclusively to micrometeoroid instrumentation. The primary experiment consisted of an array of thin-walled pressurized hemicylinders with transducers to register the pressure loss upon puncture. The puncture rate (D'Aiutolo, 1963), based on 33 punctures in 0.001-in. wall cells in four months, is shown in **Fig. 5-1**. The threshold mass was estimated on the basis of a 3 g/cm³ density and a penetration-thickness-to-particle-diameter ratio of 2. Note that the two points define a flatter curve lying several orders of magnitude below the microphone-data curve. Even if the mass were increased by a factor of 10, the difference still would be very large. One possible explanation is that the punctures are due to solid particles that constitute only a small percentage of a total flux composed mostly of fluffy or whiskerlike particles, whose penetrating ability therefore is quite low. In contrast, the microphone gages, sensitive to momentum and insensitive to density except as to possible effects on the impact back spray, would record the total flux. The puncture data were collected during the minimum of the yearly activity cycle, but this should not make a great difference.

The puncture data are of great importance in the design of spacecraft, and more flight experiments will be devoted to collection of such information. The difficulty is in having large enough areas exposed for long enough times to obtain meaningful data for thicknesses up to 0.05 in., where the flux may be down by six orders of magnitude.

The flux of micrometeoroids in the neighborhood of the Earth can also be estimated by extrapolation from radar and visual meteor data. Whipple (1963) has revised his earlier estimates for the influx of meteoroids, using a mean density of 0.44 g/cm³ and a mass of 1 g for a 30-km/sec meteoroid producing a zero-magnitude meteor. These numbers and a 0.5 correction factor for Earth shielding of a randomly oriented surface near the Earth are applied by Whipple to the photographic-meteor influx curve of Hawkins and Upton (1958) to give

$$\log I = -1.34 \log m - 14.48 , \qquad (5\text{-}4)$$

which is labeled "Whipple 1963A" in **Fig. 5-1**. Whipple assumes that this curve provides a fair representation of the cumulative mass-flux relationship down to the microphone-data region.

Hawkins (1963), using the same photographic meteor data, derives a relation which reduces to

$$\log I = -1.34 \log m - 13.39 , \qquad (5\text{-}5)$$

again expressed as particles/m²-sec and reduced by a 0.5 factor for Earth shielding; this curve is labeled "Hawkins" in **Fig. 5-1**. A zero-magnitude, 30-km/sec meteor is produced by a 4.4-g meteoroid in this analysis. Hawkins feels that the curve is accurate within a factor of 5, and that the extrapolation to the micrometeoroid range is good to an order of magnitude. Note that this curve is a factor of 10 higher than Whipple's curve. Hawkins mentions that preliminary results on the influx of radar meteors with masses greater than 4×10^{-4} g fall one order of magnitude above his suggested curve.

Levin (1963), in a study of photographic meteors, arrives at a mass of 0.09 g for a non-fragmenting 40-km/sec meteoroid producing a zero-magnitude meteor, a mass of 0.05 g for a fragmenting one, and a mass of 0.009 g for extreme fragmentation. More than 90 per cent of the analyzed meteors fragment to some extent. With a -1.34 slope, curves with these mass calibrations would fall below Whipple's by at least an order of magnitude. Levin cautions that all flux-versus-mass relationships may need revision in slope and magnitude to account for fragmention. There is no problem if all meteoroids break into the same number of pieces, but in reality the amount of fragmentation must vary with size and frangibility of the meteoroid.

Note that the mass scale has changed over two orders of magnitude recently. For example, Jacchia (1948) derived a scale of 0.15 g for a 30-km/sec, zero-magnitude meteor. The older scales were based on theoretical estimates of the conversion efficiency of kinetic energy into light. The mass scale of 25 g (Whipple, 1958) was derived on the assumption that the motion of the glowing trail is related to the momentum transfer to the trail by the meteoroid, permitting the calculation of the mass if the velocity is known (Cook and Whipple, 1958). Whipple's latest scale of 1 g is derived from the luminous efficiency of several asteroidal meteors and an artificial meteor.

Radar data, which extend to the fifteenth magnitude (Gallagher and Eshleman, 1960), indicate several trends. The random deviations in the influx rate exceed those expected statistically for particles in independent orbits. The conclusion is that there are a multitude of orbital groups, with about eleven intercepting the earth at any given time. The data show the usual seasonal variations and possibly indicate for the smaller masses an increase in numbers over the extrapolated rate. Recall that the satellite data show a high variability in influx and a steeper slope on the influx curve.

5.4. INDIRECT INDICATIONS OF MICROMETEORIC FLUX

A measure of the total mass accretion of meteoric material by the Earth is obtained from analyses of deep-sea sediments and dust collected in remote regions

(Pettersson, 1960). Most meteoritic material, by the time it reaches the Earth's surface, has been reduced to dust or to spherules of ablated material in its passage through the atmosphere. For all meteorites, the average nickel content is about 2.5 per cent. This is much higher than the nickel content of terrestrial dusts and sediments and provides a basis for the determination of the meteoritic mass influx. Present data indicate an accretion of about 5×10^6 tons per year over the entire globe, or about 3×10^{-14} g/cm²-sec. If we assume a size distribution as obtained from radar data, we conclude that most of this material arrived above the atmosphere as micrometeoroids. The figure agrees well with the total influx derived from satellite data (McCracken *et al.*, 1961). Other samplings (Crozier, 1962; Thiel and Schmidt, 1961) are in fair agreement also. This technique gives no measure of the size distribution of the primary particles or evidence of short-term temporal variations, but may indicate large fluctuations over long periods of time. The numbers probably are good to within two orders of magnitude.

A method giving more information on micrometeoroids is the study of the zodiacal light and the F component of the solar corona. The analysis shows the dust to be concentrated in the plane of the ecliptic and to extend inward to the sun. A particle-size distribution may be derived which indicates that the abundances vary as the inverse 2 to 5 power of the particle radius. Depending on the assumptions made in the analysis, the absolute values deduced from these observations for the micrometeoric flux vary by several orders of magnitude. In interplanetary space near the Earth's orbit, Beard (1959) calculates a concentration of 10^{-15} particle/cm³ for a size larger than a few microns. The concentration distribution varies as the inverse 7/2 power of particle radius, and as the inverse 3/2 power of the distance to the sun. As examples, the cumulative flux curves for the particle concentrations derived by Beard (1959), Ingham (1961), and Van de Hulst (1947) are shown in **Fig. 5-1**. The data on dust-scattered light are subject to large uncertainties. Beard assumes that the micrometeoric dust does not polarize the light, although recently it has been demonstrated that the dust may contribute significantly to the observed polarization (Geise, 1963). There are several other luminous and scattered-light effects that must be subtracted from the observations to isolate the dust-scattered component. Then the theoretical interpretation and the derivation of size and space distribution and density present calculational difficulties requiring various approximations and assumptions.

The four main sources of information still leave an uncertainty of about 10^4 in the expected micrometeoric flux near the Earth. Insufficient data, incomplete understanding of the various phenomena, and a real fluctuation in the micrometeoric concentration contribute to this large uncertainty. Beyond a few Earth radii, knowledge of the particle flux is even less certain. There are probably many unrecorded meteor streams crossing the Earth's orbit that occasionally cause large increases.

5.5. METEOR SHOWERS

Meteor showers are phenomena which tend to recur on an annual basis. Swarms of meteoroids are orbiting in space, probably roughly in the orbits of old comets. The meteoric material in most cases seems to be spread around the entire orbit, although somewhat unevenly. If the orbit intersects the Earth's orbit, a meteor shower occurs each time the Earth passes through the orbit of the meteoric material (i.e., annually). If the meteoric material is not spread around the entire orbit but concentrated in one portion of it at any one time, the showers do not occur on an annual basis; a shower will occur at the time the Earth passes through the orbit only if the meteoric material happens to be in that part of the orbit. As the meteoroids in any one group are moving through space on parallel trajectories, they all appear to come from one point in the sky, known as the radiant. The position of the radiant in the sky can be identified by use of the celestial grid, i.e., by specifying the right ascension and declination.

Meteor showers are observed both visually and with radar. When a shower occurs, the flux of micrometeoroids may be enhanced. There is direct evidence from satellite records that the Leonid stream contains a high flux of micrometeoroids (Alexander *et al.,* 1961). Vanguard 3 over several days registered impact rates up to two orders of magnitude greater than the normal with order-of-magnitude fluctuations in short time periods. Since these small sizes should not stay with the stream for even one period, these particles may have been released during perihelion passage, with the possibility of further breakup in passage through the fringes of the Earth's atmosphere before hitting the spacecraft. Some streams, as indicated by photographic and radar meteor analysis (Kaiser, 1963) show proportionately fewer small particles relative to the sporadic background. This is to be expected for old streams because of the dispersal effects discussed earlier. On the other hand, as shown by meteor fragmentation, some streams are characterized by low-strength materials that may break up near perihelion and replenish the microparticle component.

A list of the meteoroid streams that give rise to meteor showers is given in Table 5-1. Also given in this table are the times at which the showers occur, the positions of the radiants, the meteoroid velocities relative to the Earth, and the maximum rates of occurrence of radio-echo meteors for the more intense known

TABLE 5-1

METEOROID STREAMS

Shower	Date of Maximum	Limits	Radiant R.A. (°)	Radiant Dec. (°)	Velocity (km/sec)	Maximum Hourly Radar Echo Rate
Quadrantids	Jan. 3	Jan. 1–Jan. 4	230	+48	42.7	95
Virginids	Mar. 13	Mar. 5–Mar. 21	183	+ 4	30.8	< 5
Lyrids	Apr. 21	Apr. 20–Apr. 23	270	+33	48.4	11
η Aquarids	May 4	May 2–May 6	336	+ 0	64	15
Daytime Arietids	June 8	May 29–June 18	44	+23	39	66
Daytime ζ Perseids	June 9	June 1–June 16	62	+23	29	42
Sagittarids	June 11		304	−35		30
Daytime β Taurids	June 30	June 24–July 6	86	+19	32	27
Phoenicids	July 14		32	−48		30
Southern δ Aquarids	July 30	July 21–Aug. 15	339	−17	43.0 ⎫	34
Northern δ Aquarids		July 14–Aug. 19	339	− 5	42.3 ⎭	
Southern ι Aquarids		July 16–Aug. 25	338	−14	35.8	
Northern ι Aquarids		July 16–Aug. 25	331	− 5	31.2	
α Capricornids	Aug. 1	July 17–Aug. 21	309	−10	25.5	10
Perseids	Aug. 12	July 29–Aug. 17	46	+58	60.4	49
κ Cygnids		Aug. 19–Aug. 22	289	+56	26.6	< 5
Draconids	Oct. 10	Oct. 10	264	+54	23.1	Periodic
Orionids	Oct. 22	Oct. 18–Oct. 26	94	+16	66.5	18
Southern Taurids	Nov. 1	Sept. 15–Dec. 15	51	+14	30.2 ⎫	<15
Northern Taurids	Nov. 10	Oct. 17–Dec. 2	52	+21	31.3 ⎭	
Andromedids	Nov. 7	Nov. 7	22	+27	21.3	< 5
Leonids	Nov. 17	Nov. 14–Nov. 20	152	+22	72.0	<10
Puppids/Velids	Dec. 6	Dec. 1–Dec. 9	140	−50		50
Geminids	Dec. 14	Dec. 7–Dec. 15	113	+32	36.5	80
χ Orionids		Dec. 9–Dec. 14	87	+21	30.6	
Monocerotids		Dec. 13–Dec. 15	103	+ 8	44.0	
Ursids	Dec. 22	Dec. 17–Dec. 24	206	+80	35.2	13

showers (McIntosh, 1935; Weiss, 1960; Whipple and Hawkins, 1959). The comparable sporadic rate is about 10 meteors/hr. Many other streams whose orbits do not intersect the Earth's orbit can be expected in space.

5.6. PENETRATION

As yet there is insufficient information to reasonably evaluate the dangers to spacecraft in the micrometeoric environment. For masses less than 10^{-7} g, it is mainly a problem of erosion of optical surfaces, solar cells, surfaces of selected emissivity, and the like. Meteoroid masses in the range of 10^{-7} to 10^{-4} g are of a size and frequency likely to endanger space vehicles. Accompanied by spallation and meteoroid fragments, punctures in fuel tanks or space cabins could be cata-strophic. The very few direct-penetration data are in a mass range much lower than that of interest for long-term missions. The area–time exposures required to obtain this information directly are very high, and therefore much reliance must be placed on laboratory and theoretical investigations. Laboratory simula-tion of meteoroids is just reaching the lower velocity limits for meteoric impact. It is difficult to accelerate low-density and low-strength materials comparable to much of the conjectured space debris. Still in their infancy, the various theo-retical explanations of the impact phenomena require experimental results at higher velocities for assessment of their validity. Complicating the problem of evaluating the hazard is the lack of knowledge of the velocity distributions, struc-tures, and densities and materials of the meteoroids in space.

Whipple (1963) presents a penetration probability curve derived from what he considers the best available data. He gives the average time between penetra-tions against skin thickness for aluminum, and these data are shown in **Fig. 5-2.**

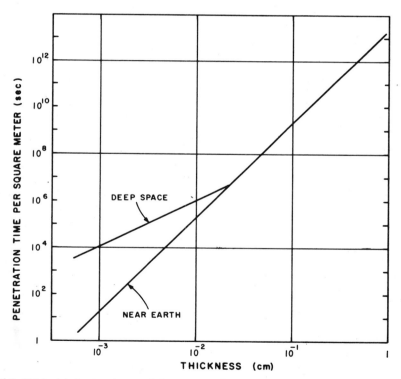

Fig. 5-2. Whipple's best estimate of the average time between penetrations of 1 m² of alu-minum skin of various thicknesses. The average meteoroid density was taken to be 0.44 g/cm³.

(For steel the times are about ten times longer.) On the basis of more recent meteor experiments and hypervelocity impact results, he has lowered his earlier estimate of the hazard (Whipple, 1958) by a factor of about 3000. The extrapolations of the density to low values and the cratering equations to meteoric velocities are questionable, but Whipple suggests an order of magnitude accuracy for the curve. Recall that Hawkins's influx curve is an order of magnitude above Whipple's, but on the other hand the Explorer 16 results fall close to the deep space curve in **Fig. 5-2**.

The decrease in micrometeoric flux with distance from the Earth is very uncertain in magnitude and slope, but most indications are that the hazard is significantly less away from the Earth except in the near vicinity of the moon. Around other planets the concentrations can only be guessed at, and they may depend on the presence of a natural satellite. As one moves toward the sun, the relative velocities and particle concentrations increase. In the other direction, the asteroidal region may present an increased danger. Finally, there are man's own contributions to the hazards—one, for example, in the form of orbiting dipoles (Morrow and MacLellan, 1961).

REFERENCES

Alexander, W. M. 1962. "The Mission of Mariner II: Preliminary Observations, Cosmic Dust," *Science,* **138**, 1098.

Alexander, W. M., C. W. McCracken, and H. E. LaGow. 1961. "Interplanetary Dust Particles of Micron-Size Probably Associated with the Leonid Meteor Stream," *J. Geophys. Research,* **66**, 3970–73.

Beard, D. B. 1959. "Interplanetary Dust Distribution," *Astrophys. J.,* **129**, 496–506.

Beard, D. B. 1961. "The Dust Cloud about the Earth," *Nature,* **191**, 32–33.

Best, G. T., and T. N. L. Patterson. 1962. "The Capture of Small Absorbing Particles by the Solar Radiation Field," *Planet. Space Sci.,* **9**, 801–9.

Cook, A. F., and F. L. Whipple. 1958. Unpublished (see F. L. Whipple and G. S. Hawkins, 1959, "Meteors," *Handbuch der Physik,* **52**, 519–64; G. S. Hawkins and E. K. L. Upton, 1958, "The Influx Rate of Meteors in the Earth's Atmosphere," *Astrophys. J.,* **128**, 727–35).

Crozier, W. D. 1962. "Five Years of Continuous Collection of Black, Magnetic Spherules from the Atmosphere," *J. Geophys. Research,* **67**, 2543–48.

D'Aiutolo, C. T. 1963. "Review of Meteoroid Environment Based on Results from Explorer XIII and Explorer XVI Satellites." Paper presented at the Fourth International Space Sciences Symposium of COSPAR, Warsaw, Poland, June 3–12, 1963.

de Jager, C. 1955. "The Capture of Zodiacal Dust by the Earth," *Mémoires de la Société Royale des Sciences de Liége,* **15**, 174–82.

Dole, S. H. 1962. "The Gravitational Concentration of Particles in Space near the Earth," *Planet. Space Sci.,* **9**, 541–53.

Donn, B., and G. W. Sears. 1963. "Planets and Comets: Role of Crystal Growth in Their Formation," *Science,* **140**, 1208–11.

Dubin, M., and C. W. McCracken. 1962. "Measurements of Distributions of Interplanetary Dust," *Astron. J.,* **67**, 248–56.

Gallagher, P. B., and V. R. Eshleman. 1960. " 'Sporadic Shower' Properties of Very Small Meteors," *J. Geophys. Research,* **65,** 1846–47.

Gault, D. E., E. D. Heitowit, and H. J. Moore. 1963a. "Some Observations of Hypervelocity Impacts with Porous Media," NASA Tech. Mem. X-54009 (to be published in *Proceedings,* Lunar Surface Materials Conference, Boston, Mass., May 21–23, 1963).

Gault, D. E., E. M. Shoemaker, and H. J. Moore. 1963b. "Spray Ejected from the Lunar Surface by Meteoroid Impact," NASA Tech. Note D-1767.

Geise, R. H. 1963. "Light Scattering by Small Particles and Models of Interplanetary Matter Derived from the Zodiacal Light," *Space Science Reviews,* **1,** 589–611.

Hapke, B., and H. Van Horn. 1963. "Photometric Studies of Complex Surfaces, with Applications to the Moon," *J. Geophys. Research,* **68,** 4544–70.

Harwit, M. 1963. "Origins of the Zodiacal Dust Cloud," *J. Geophys. Research,* **68,** 2171–80.

Hastings, E. C., Jr. 1963. "The Explorer XVI Micrometeoroid Satellite. Supplement I, Preliminary Results for the Period Jan. 14, 1963, through March 2, 1963," NASA Tech. Mem. X-824.

Hawkins, G. S., and E. K. L. Upton. 1958. "The Influx Rate of Meteors in the Earth's Atmosphere," *Astrophys. J.,* **128,** 727–35.

Hawkins, G. S. 1963. "The Meteor Population," Res. Rept. No. 3, The Harvard Radio Meteor Project, Smithsonian Astrophysical Observatory, Cambridge, Mass.

Hemenway, C. L., and R. K. Soberman. 1962. "Studies of Micrometeorites Obtained from a Recoverable Sounding Rocket," *Astron. J.,* **67,** 256–66.

Hibbs, A. R. 1961. "The Distribution of Micrometeorites near the Earth," *J. Geophys. Research,* **66,** 371–77.

Hibbs, A. R. 1963. "A Hypothesis that the Surface of the Moon Is Covered with Needle Crystals," *Icarus,* **2,** 181–86.

Ingham, M. F. 1961. "Observations of the Zodiacal Light from a Very High Altitude Station. IV. The Nature and Distribution of the Interplanetary Dust," *Monthly Notices, Roy. Astron. Soc.,* **122,** 157–76.

Jacchia, L. G. 1948. "Harvard Coll. Observatory Reprint Ser. II," No. 26 (see F. L. Whipple and G. S. Hawkins, 1959, "Meteors," *Handbuch der Physik,* **52,** 519–64).

Jacchia, L. G. 1963. "Meteors, Meteorites and Comets: Interrelations," in B. M. Middlehurst and G. P. Kuiper, eds., *The Moon, Meteorites and Comets.* University of Chicago Press, pp. 774–98.

Kaiser, T. R. 1963. "Meteors and the Abundance of Interplanetary Matter," *Space Science Reviews,* **1,** 554–75.

Levin, B. Yu. 1963. "Fragmentation of Meteoric Bodies," *Soviet Astron.–AJ,* **7,** 233–42.

McCracken, C. W., W. M. Alexander, and M. Dubin. 1961. "Direct Measurements of Interplanetary Dust Particles in the Vicinity of Earth," *Nature,* **192,** 441–42.

McIntosh, R. A. 1935. "An Index to Southern Meteor Showers," *Monthly Notices, Roy. Astron. Soc.,* **95,** 709–18.

Moroz, V. I. 1963. "The Dust Cloud about the Earth," *Planet. Space Sci.,* **11,** 387–94.

Morrow, W. E., Jr., and D. C. MacLellan. 1961. "Properties of Orbiting Dipole Belts," *Astron. J.,* **66,** 107–13.

Nazarova, T. N. 1963. "The Investigation of Meteoric Dust by Means of Rockets and Artificial Earth Satellites," *Planet. Space Sci.,* **11,** 305–9.

Pettersson, Hans. 1960. "Cosmic Spherules and Meteoritic Dust," *Scientific American,* **202,** No. 2, 123–32.

Robertson, H. P. 1937. "Dynamical Effects of Radiation in the Solar System," *Monthly Notices, Roy. Astron. Soc.,* **97,** 423–38.

Ruskol, Ye. L. 1963. "The Origin of the Concentration of Interplanetary Dust about the Earth," *Planet. Space Sci.,* **11,** 311–16.

Singer, S. F. 1961. "Interplanetary Dust near the Earth," *Nature*, 192, 321–23.

Singer, S. F. 1962. "Effects of Nongravitational Forces on Zodiacal Dust" (Abstract), *J. Geophys. Research*, 67, 3599.

Southworth, R. B. 1963. "On S. H. Dole's Paper 'The Gravitational Concentration of Particles in Space near the Earth,'" *Planet. Space Sci.*, 11, 499–503.

Thiel, E., and R. A. Schmidt. 1961. "Spherules from the Antarctic Ice Cap," *J. Geophys. Research*, 66, 307–10.

Van de Hulst, H. C. 1947. "Zodiacal Light in the Solar Corona," *Astrophys. J.*, 105, 471–88.

Varsavsky, C. M. 1958. "Dynamical Limits on a Lunar Origin for Tektites," *Geochim. et Cosmochim. Acta*, 14, 291–303.

Wehner, G. K., C. E. KenKnight, and D. L. Rosenberg. 1963a. "Sputtering Rates under Solar-Wind Bombardment," *Planet. Space Sci.*, 11, 885–95.

Wehner, G. K., C. E. KenKnight, and D. L. Rosenberg. 1963b. "Modification of the Lunar Surface by the Solar-Wind Bombardment," *Planet. Space Sci.*, 11, 1257–61.

Weiss, A. A. 1960. "Radio-Echo Observations of Southern Hemisphere Meteor Shower Activity," *Monthly Notices, Roy. Astron. Soc.*, 120, 387–403.

Whipple, F. L. 1950. "A Comet Model. I. The Acceleration of Comet Encke," *Astrophys. J.*, 111, 375–94.

Whipple, F. L. 1955. "A Comet Model. III. The Zodiacal Light," *Astrophys. J.*, 121, 750–70.

Whipple, F. L. 1958. "The Meteoritic Risk to Space Vehicles," in M. Alperin and M. Stern, eds., *Vistas in Astronautics*. Pergamon, London, pp. 115–24.

Whipple, F. L. 1961. "The Dust Cloud about the Earth," *Nature*, 189, 127–28.

Whipple, F. L. 1963. "On Meteoroids and Penetration," *J. Geophys. Research*, 68, 4929–39.

Whipple, F. L., and G. S. Hawkins. 1959. "Meteors," *Handbuch der Physik*, 52, 519–64.

Wyatt, S. P., Jr., and F. L. Whipple. 1950. "The Poynting-Robertson Effect on Meteor Orbits," *Astrophys. J.*, 111, 134–41.

6. Radio Noise

H. C. Ko

Radio Observatory, Department of Electrical Engineering,
Ohio State University, Columbus, Ohio

6. Radio Noise

H. C. Ko

Radio Observatory, Department of Electrical Engineering,
Ohio State University, Columbus, Ohio

6.1. INTRODUCTION

Noise can be defined as any random signal that interferes with the detection of a desired signal. Noise occurs quite spontaneously in every measuring system or apparatus. The effect of any type of noise is to limit the minimum signal level that the system can detect satisfactorily. The noise present in a radio receiving system may have originated at a number of sources, and by a number of different physical processes. Table 6-1 lists the major sources of radio noise and classifies these sources according to whether they are external or internal to the receiver and its antenna.

TABLE 6-1

MAJOR SOURCES OF NOISE

External Noise	Internal Noise
Atmospheric static	Thermal noise
Terrestrial thermal radio noise	Shot noise
Atmospheric thermal radio noise	Flicker noise
Ionospheric thermal radio noise	Semiconductor noise
VLF radio emissions	
Cosmic radio noise	
Lunar and planetary radio noise	
Solar radio noise	
Man-made noise and interference	

The external radio noise may be generated on the Earth, in its upper atmosphere, and in cosmic space. This noise can penetrate the Earth's upper atmosphere, which is transparent to radio waves over a wide frequency range extending from about 5 Mc/s up to about 30,000 Mc/s. Radio signals above 30,000 Mc/s are absorbed by the molecules in the Earth's atmosphere, while the signals below about 5 Mc/s are totally reflected by the Earth's ionosphere.

The observed intensity of noise sources listed in Table 6-1 varies considerably with frequency, and for some sources of noise it also varies with the relative location of the receiver with respect to the origins of the sources. Therefore, in order to estimate the relative contribution of various sources of noise to a receiving system, it is necessary to consider the frequency of reception, the propagation path, and the geometry of the receiving system.

Without noise, a signal, however faint it might be, could be amplified indefinitely until the desired output power is obtained. Thus, to the communication engineer attempting to achieve the ultimate system sensitivity, the noise is a limitation. However, some of the external noise, such as cosmic radio noise, solar radio noise, VLF emissions, is a valuable source of astronomical information. From a careful analysis and study of the nature of this noise, the new science of radio astronomy has already brought out much new knowledge on the astronomical universe during the last decade. Until very recently, radio astronomical observations were made from the ground, and thus were restricted to the frequency bands inside the radio window in the Earth's atmosphere. But since the advent of high-altitude rockets, satellites, and space probes, the limitations of the radio window are now gradually vanishing. By flying radio telescopes in a satellite or space probe, it is now possible to observe those frequency bands outside the radio window of the atmosphere.

It is convenient to use an equivalent temperature concept to represent the intensity of various noise sources. The noise power available from a resistor at a temperature T ($°K$) over a frequency band Δf is given by

$$P = kT\Delta f , \tag{6-1}$$

where k is Boltzmann's constant. The internal noise level of a receiver may thus be represented by an effective receiver noise temperature

$$T_R = P/(k\Delta f) , \tag{6-2}$$

where P is the noise generated by the receiver.

Similarly, the available noise power from an antenna due to external sources may be represented by an equivalent temperature of a matched resistor whose available noise power is equal to that of the antenna. This is often referred to as the *antenna temperature, T_A*. A blackbody radiates radio noise according to the Rayleigh-Jeans Law in the radio-frequency range, and the noise intensity is proportional to the temperature of the body. Thus,

$$B = 2kT/\lambda^2 , \tag{6-3}$$

where B is the intensity or brightness and λ is the wavelength. Therefore the noise intensity of an external noise source may be represented by an equivalent temperature of a blackbody which has the same noise intensity as that of the source. This is often referred to as the *brightness temperature* of the source. When an antenna with an effective collecting aperture $A(\theta, \phi)$ in the direction (θ, ϕ) is surrounded by randomly polarized external noise sources of brightness temperature $T_B(\theta, \phi)$, the antenna temperature T_A may be computed by

$$T_A = \frac{1}{\lambda^2} \int \int_{4\pi} A(\theta, \phi) T_B(\theta, \phi) d\Omega . \tag{6-4}$$

The total noise in a receiving system is then represented by the sum of the two temperatures, $T_A + T_R$, and this is sometimes called the *effective system noise temperature.*

The use of the equivalent temperature concepts is particularly convenient in the analysis and comparison of electric noise, electromagnetic noise, and low-noise communication systems. A coherent discussion on the use of temperature concepts in modern radio has been given in detail by Ko (1961).

6.2. ATMOSPHERIC STATIC

Atmospheric static is generated by natural electrical disturbances such as lightning, and consists in general of short pulses with random recurrence superimposed upon a background of random noise. The propagation of static is markedly affected by the ionospheric conditions. The noise thus produced varies in intensity with frequency, time of day, season, geographical location, and weather. Crichlow *et al.* (1955) have prepared very useful information on the expected median values of worldwide static noise levels.

The intensity of atmospheric static falls off rapidly with frequency, and is usually of little consequence at higher frequencies. At frequencies below 15 Mc/s, static is the dominant source of all external noise in ground-based receiving systems. Since the ionosphere prevents static from propagating outside of the ionosphere, static becomes unimportant in receiver design for high-altitude satellites and space probes.

6.3. ATMOSPHERIC THERMAL NOISE

Kirchhoff's laws of radiation show that any body that absorbs energy radiates the same amount of energy that it absorbs under thermal equilibrium. Thus the Earth's atmosphere is a source of thermal radiation, since it absorbs microwave energies at frequencies above 30 kMc/s. The intensity of thermal noise is proportional to the path length, thus being maximum when looking along the horizon and minimum when looking up toward the zenith. In the 1 to 10 kMc/s band in which most space communication systems operate, the effective noise

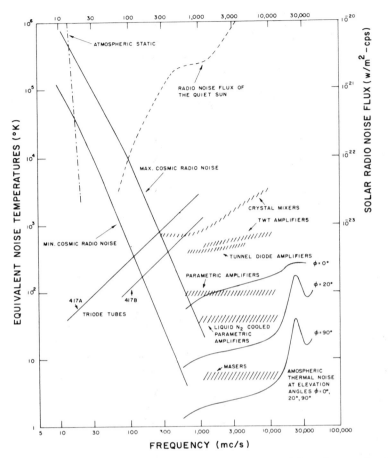

Fig. 6-1. Comparison of the intensity of the principal sources of radio noise as a function of frequency. The intensity is expressed in terms of equivalent noise temperatures. The intensity of the quiet sun is expressed in terms of the flux density.

temperature increases from about 3 °K to 100 °K as the zenith angle is increased from 0° to 90°. The intensity also varies greatly with the frequency, as shown in **Fig. 6-1**. The microwave absorption is mainly due to water vapor and oxygen in the atmosphere. Both theoretically calculated values and experimentally measured values are now available for the estimation of the atmospheric thermal noise (Hogg and Mumford, 1960).

The atmospheric thermal noise plays an important role in the threshold noise level at frequencies above 5 kMc/s when the atmosphere is a part of the wave propagation path, such as in the case of the satellite-to-ground link or the ground-based radio telescope.

6.4. IONOSPHERIC THERMAL NOISE

The Earth's ionosphere also emits thermal radiation due to ionospheric absorption, which occurs mostly in the regions below the E layer. The intensity of thermal noise from the ionosphere corresponds to an effective noise brightness temperature of about 300 °K at 2 Mc/s, and falls off very rapidly with frequency, becoming negligible above 50 Mc/s. However, the intensity below 50 Mc/s is very small compared with that of cosmic radio noise and atmospheric static, and therefore can be ignored in the estimation of the total noise in the receiving system. The direct detection of the ionospheric thermal noise has been made under very quiet atmospheric static conditions (Gardner, 1954). Such a measurement can be used to derive information about the temperature of the absorbing part of the ionosphere.

6.5. VLF EMISSIONS

Radio waves in the frequency band from 1 to 20 kc/s are generated in the Earth's exosphere, and they propagate along the Earth's magnetic field lines in the manner of whistlers (Gallet, 1959; Ellis, 1963). Unlike whistlers, which are caused by terrestrial lightning strokes, the very low-frequency emission is excited in the exosphere by streams and bunches of high-energy ionized particles. These particles may be trapped in the magnetic field in the ionized exosphere, and they execute oscillations back and forth along the field lines between the magnetic mirror points. During their motion, the electrons emit radio noise, probably by the cyclotron process or by the traveling-wave-tube mechanism. The frequency band in which the emission occurs depends on the local electron density in the exosphere, the local magnetic field intensity, and the particle velocity. There appear to be two classes of VLF emissions: discrete emissions which occupy a bandwidth of about 1 kc/s lasting a few seconds, and continuous emissions which occupy a wide band of frequency lasting over several hours. The occurrence of VLF emissions is correlated with the periods of magnetic disturbance and the arrival of solar corpuscular radiation in the vicinity of the Earth. The VLF emissions thus provide a new way for the study of the dynamic properties of the charged particles in the exosphere.

6.6. COSMIC RADIO NOISE

Cosmic radio noise is natural radiation of extraterrestrial origin in the radio-frequency portion of the electromagnetic spectrum. Such radiation was first discovered by Karl Jansky in 1932 while studying the direction of arrival of atmo-

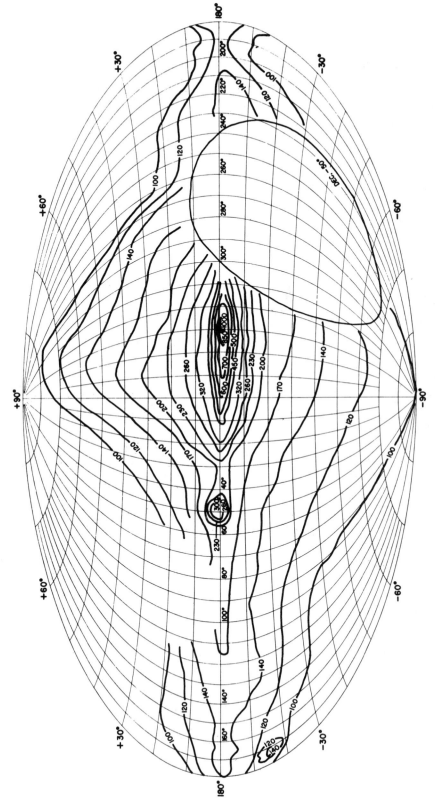

Fig. 6-2. 250 Mc/s radio contours of the cosmic radio noise in galactic coordinates. The numbers on the contours give the absolute brightness temperature in degrees Kelvin. *Ko* (1958), *reproduced with permission of Institute of Radio Engineers.*

spheric static at 20.5 Mc/s. Since most of the astronomical information about the universe had previously been gained by optical observations, the existence of the cosmic radio waves opened an entirely new possibility for the exploration of the universe. The radiation consists of continuous radiation extending practically over the whole radio-frequency range and a line emission restricted to a very narrow frequency near 1420 Mc/s. Observations of the continuous radiation are now available from 0.5 Mc/s up to 30,000 Mc/s. Until recently, because of the ionospheric cutoff, observations at the lowest frequencies could be made on the ground only under very favorable ionospheric conditions (Reber, 1958). However, rocket- or satellite-borne receivers have been employed recently to obtain useful data (Walsh *et al.,* 1963; Molozzi *et al.,* 1961) at frequencies below the ionospheric critical frequency. The equivalent blackbody brightness temperature of the cosmic noise decreases with frequency according to the reciprocal nth power of the frequency, where n is called the *spectral index* and is about 2.7, as shown in **Fig. 6-1**.

The intensity distribution of cosmic noise over the sky may be classified into two categories: (1) radiation from discrete sources (i.e., radio stars), and (2) a general background radiation not resolvable into discrete sources. The background radiation is strongly concentrated along the galactic equator and particularly toward the galactic center. Many radio maps of the sky have been completed at various frequencies, and a summary of their pertinent data has been given by Ko (1958). **Figure 6-2** shows a sample radio map made at 250 Mc/s.

The mechanism of the continuous radiation consists of at least two distinct processes, one of which is the well-known thermal process involving bremsstrahlung from the ionized interstellar hydrogen gas, the other being the nonthermal process involving synchrotron radiation from relativistic electrons moving in the galactic magnetic field. Over nearly all the sky the observed cosmic noise at frequencies below 300 Mc/s is mainly dominated by the nonthermal component. At much higher frequency, the thermal component begins to dominate the rapidly decreasing nonthermal component.

Over a thousand discrete radio sources or radio stars are known today. The angular size varies from less than a few minutes of arc to over several degrees. The measured flux density ranges from 10^{-22} to 10^{-26} watts/m²-cps. Some discrete sources are objects in our own galaxy, and have been identified with various optical objects such as H II regions, supernovae remnants, etc. However, a large portion of the discrete sources are extragalactic objects, and a few of these sources have been identified with normal and abnormal galaxies. For a more detailed discussion on cosmic radio noise, the reader is referred to Shklovsky (1960) and Steinberg and Lequeux (1963).

For a ground-based receiving system, the cosmic background radio noise is a dominant source of noise in the frequency range between 50 Mc/s and 1000 Mc/s. However, for a space-bound receiver, cosmic noise becomes the primary source of external noise over the entire radio-frequency spectrum.

6.7. LUNAR AND PLANETARY RADIO NOISE

Radio emissions from the moon and from several planets including Venus, Mars, Saturn, Mercury, and Jupiter have been studied in some detail (Mayer, 1961). The radio emission provides a new source of information about these bodies and their atmospheres.

The radio observations of the moon indicate that the radio brightness temperature varies slightly with the lunar phase, and the averaged brightness temperature at the center of the lunar disk is about 210 °K.

The radio emission from the planets Venus, Mars, Saturn, and Mercury is of the thermal type, and the brightness disk temperatures are found to be about 580 °K, 218 °K, 106 °K, and 400 °K, respectively. The radio emission from Jupiter is of an entirely different kind—the brightness temperature rises from about 150 °K at 10,000 Mc/s to about 50,000 °K at 400 Mc/s, indicating the nonthermal nature of the radiation. The radiation at 900 Mc/s is about 30 per cent linearly polarized, with its electric vector approximately parallel to the Jovian equator. Another type of radio noise is also observed from Jupiter at lower frequencies near 20 Mc/s; this is of burst type and occurs sporadically.

Because of its low flux density, the radio noise from the moon and the planets is seldom an important factor in the design of space communication systems. However, for space probes designed to fly near the moon or the planets, the noise from these bodies should be taken into account in the system design.

6.8. SOLAR RADIO NOISE

Radio emission from the sun has been studied systematically since 1946, and these studies have usefully contributed to our knowledge of the physical state and the large-scale structure of the corona and the chromosphere.

In the visible wavelengths, where the sun emits most of its energy, the total radiated power varies very little, at most 1 or 2 per cent. By contrast, however, the radio emission is highly variable, often exceeding the undisturbed intensity by several orders of magnitude. It is convenient to divide solar radio emissions into two components: a weak and relatively constant component from the undisturbed or quiet sun, and a variable component from the disturbed sun. The variable component may in turn be subdivided into a slowly varying component having periods of days, weeks, or months, and a rapidly varying component characterized by bursts lasting over seconds, minutes, or hours.

Radio emission from the quiet sun is believed to be of thermal origin. The

apparent disk temperature of the quiet sun at centimeter wavelengths is about
3×10^4 °K, increasing with wavelength to about 10^6 °K at meter wavelengths.
This temperature variation is due to the fact that the emission originates in
higher and hotter layers of the ionized solar atmosphere as the wavelength becomes longer.

It is very rare for the radio sun to be perfectly quiet, because of the presence
of the slowly varying component. The slowly varying component is of thermal
origin and originates in the active regions on the solar surface containing facu-
lar plages and spots. The emission is remarkably stable, lasting days, weeks, or
even months, and is most evident in the centimeter and decimeter wavelengths.
Over the period of a sunspot cycle, the slowly varying component correlates very
well with the sunspot number, and the contribution from the slowly varying
component during the sunspot maximum may reach several times the intensity
of the quiet sun. In **Fig. 6-3**, the monthly means of 10.7-cm radio-noise flux

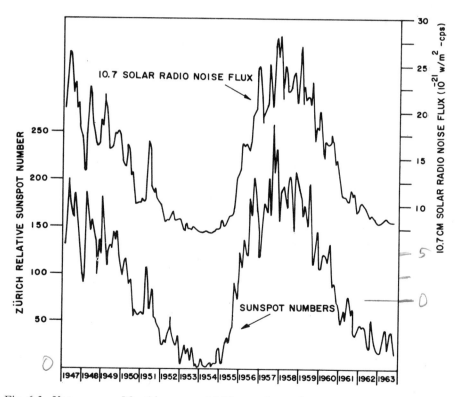

Fig. 6-3. *Upper curve:* Monthly means of 10.7-cm solar radio-noise flux recorded by Cov-
ington at National Research Council, Ottawa, Canada (units are 10^{-21} watts/m²-cps). *Lower
curve:* Monthly means of the Zürich relative sunspot numbers from 1947 to 1963.

from the sun are plotted, together with the Zürich relative sunspot numbers. It is known that there is an extremely close correlation between the centimeter solar flux and the state of the ionospheric E layer.

The rapidly varying component consists of rapidly varying bursts of emission, and is associated with solar flares. Solar bursts have been observed over a wide range of wavelengths, from less than 1 cm (30 kMc/s) to about 50 m (6 Mc/s). Bursts in the microwave region (or microwave bursts) and those in the meter wavelengths (or meter-wave bursts) show sharp contrasting features in their characteristics. The microwave bursts are generally weak and of short duration, while the meter-wave bursts are intense and rich in variety. Solar bursts have been classified into five distinctive types, according to different frequency and time characteristics, as listed in Table 6-2. Solar bursts are quite spectacular, particularly at the meter wavelengths. The effective disk temperature of the sun rises and fluctuates as much as a thousand to a million times the value of the quiet sun.

The frequency dependence of the intensity of solar radio noise is illustrated in **Fig. 6-1**. For more complete information on the nature and mechanisms of solar radio noise, the reader is referred to Steinberg and Lequeux (1963) and Wild *et al.* (1963).

TABLE 6-2

CHARACTERISTICS OF THE PRINCIPAL TYPES OF SOLAR RADIO BURSTS

Type	Description
I	Noise storms consisting of very numerous bursts of short duration (a few seconds). Duration of storm, hours to days. Occur on meter wavelengths only. Circularly polarized.
II	Slow-drift bursts. Broad-band noise (about 50 Mc/s), drifting slowing from high to low frequencies (drift rate about 20 Mc/s per minute). Average duration, about 5 to 30 minutes. Occur on meter and decimeter wavelengths. Usually unpolarized.
III	Fast-drift bursts. Narrow-band noise (about 5 Mc/s), drifting rapidly from high to low frequencies (drift rate about 20 Mc/s per second). Duration of individual bursts, about 10 seconds. Occur on meter and decimeter wavelengths. Usually unpolarized.
IV	Prolonged continuum noise of high intensity. Duration, 10 minutes to hours. Occur on the meter, decimeter, and centimeter wavelengths. Often circularly polarized. Strong association with solar proton emission events.
V	Broad-band continuum noise. Duration, several minutes. Occur on meter wavelengths only. Sometimes elliptically polarized.

The effect of solar radio noise on the receiver sensitivity is in general not too great because of the small angular extent of the sun. However, solar noise can be a serious source of interference for a large antenna system that is pointing at the sun. The antenna noise temperature due to the sun may be calculated by $T_A = SA/2k$, where S is the flux density of the solar radio noise, A is the antenna collecting area, and k is the Boltzmann constant.

6.9. MAN-MADE NOISE AND INTERFERENCE

Noise from automobile ignition, electric razors, fluorescent lights, house appliances, power lines, and industrial machines are examples of man-made noise. The intensity of this noise is greatest in cities and industrialized areas and in general falls off rapidly with frequency.

Another important factor to be considered is interference from other radar and communication services to the satellite communication system or to other space research instruments such as radio telescopes. Although the character of the interference signals is unlike random noise, the interference is often considered to be noise. Today the Earth is covered with a great number of high- and low-power transmitters, which provide various services for civilian, military, and scientific needs at all frequency bands. The combined effect of all these services gives rise to a background interference level. In general, the effects of an interfering signal must be determined for each system, since the tolerable interference level depends greatly upon the type of receiving system, the geographical location, etc.

Proper frequency allocations on an international basis are absolutely essential for the successful operation of space communication systems and space-research experiments. In 1963 the Geneva Space Radio Communication Conference, convened by the International Telecommunication Union, allocated on a shared or exclusive basis frequencies totaling 6076.462 Mc/s in bandwidth for the various kinds of space services, 2800 Mc/s of which are for communication satellites on a shared basis with other services. This total bandwidth is about 15 per cent of the total radio-frequency spectrum.

The problem of interference becomes more acute when the frequency for satellite communication is shared by other services. Such frequency-sharing becomes necessary because of the large bandwidth required for satellite communication in already crowded regions of the spectrum. The results of the study of frequency allocation and interference for space communication, space-research, and radio-astronomy experiments have been summarized in detail by Brown (1962).

6.10. RECEIVER NOISE

Receiver noise refers to the noise generated within the radio receiver. The physical mechanisms of the noise are many, among which the thermal noise, shot noise, flicker noise, and semiconductor noise are well known. The noise also occurs at various parts of the receiver, and is often identified as mixer noise, local-oscillator noise, amplifier noise, etc. In conventional receivers employing regular electron tubes and diode mixers, the receiver noise goes up with the frequency, as shown in **Fig. 6-1**. Since the intensity of the external noise falls off rapidly with the frequency, the sensitivity of a conventional receiver is limited by the external noise at lower frequencies and by the receiver noise at higher frequencies. However, the invention and successful operation of many new low-noise amplifiers such as masers, parametric amplifiers, and tunnel diode amplifiers have greatly improved the receiver-noise temperature at microwave frequencies. Receiver-noise temperatures of less than 20 °K have been achieved in practical systems. Thus the sensitivity of modern receiving systems is now frequently limited by the external noise.

Antenna noise due to sources in the atmosphere and cosmic space is beyond the control of the antenna engineers. However, the antenna noise due to pickup of ground thermal radiation can be greatly reduced with a careful antenna design. A number of low-noise antennas are in use today (Ko, 1964).

Considering the contributions of all the external and internal noise sources (see **Fig. 6-1**), the frequency range between 1 and 10 kMc/s appears to be most suitable for operation of space communication systems.

REFERENCES

Brown, G. M. 1962. *Space Radio Communication*. Elsevier Publishing Co., New York.

Crichlow, W. Q., D. F. Smith, R. N. Morton, and W. R. Corliss. 1955. "Worldwide Radio Noise Levels Expected in the Frequency Band 10 Kc to 100 Mc." National Bureau of Standards Circular 557, U.S. Government Printing Office, Washington, D.C.

Ellis, G. R. A. 1963. "The VLF Radio Emissions from the Earth's Outer Atmosphere," *Proc. I.R.E. Australia,* **24,** 205.

Gallet, R. M. 1959. "The Very Low-Frequency Emissions Generated in the Earth's Exosphere," *Proc. I.R.E.,* **47,** 211.

Gardner, F. F. 1954. "Ionosphere Thermal Radiation at Radio Frequencies. II. Further Observations," *J. Atmos. Terr. Phys.,* **5,** 298.

Hogg, D. C., and W. W. Mumford. 1960. "The Effective Noise Temperature of the Sky," *Microwave Journal,* **3,** 80.

Ko, H. C. 1958. "The Distribution of Cosmic Radio Background Radiation," *Proc. I.R.E.,* **46,** 208–15.

Ko, H. C. 1961. "Temperature Concepts in Modern Radio," *Microwave Journal,* **4,** 60.

Ko, H. C. 1964. "Radio-Telescope Antennas," in R. C. Hansen, ed., *Microwave Scanning Antennas.* Academic Press, New York.

Mayer, C. H. 1961. "Radio Emission of the Moon and Planets," in G. P. Kuiper, ed., *The Solar System,* Vol. III. University of Chicago Press, chap. 12.

Molozzi, A. R., C. A. Franklin, and J. P. I. Tyas. 1961. "Cosmic Noise Measurements from 1960 ηI at 3.8 Mc/s," *Nature,* **190,** 616.

Reber, G. 1958. "Between the Atmospheric," *J. Geophys. Research,* **63,** 109.

Shklovsky, I. S. 1960. *Cosmic Radio Waves.* Harvard University Press, Cambridge, Mass.

Steinberg, J. L., and J. Lequeux. 1963. *Radio Astronomy.* McGraw-Hill, New York.

Walsh, D., F. T. Haddock, and H. F. Schulte. 1963. "Cosmic Radio Intensities at 1.225 and 2.0 Mc/s Measured up to an Altitude of 1700 Km." Fourth International Space Science Symposium, Warsaw, Poland.

Wild, J. P., S. F. Smerd, and A. A. Weiss. 1963. "Solar Bursts," *Annual Review of Astronomy and Astrophysics* (Annual Reviews Inc., Palo Alto, Calif.), **1,** 291–366.

7. Thermal Radiation from the Earth

Francis S. Johnson

Southwest Center for Advanced Studies, Dallas

7. Thermal Radiation from the Earth

Francis S. Johnson

Southwest Center for Advanced Studies, Dallas

7.1. INTRODUCTION

The problem of selecting reasonable values for radiation from the Earth is quite complicated when one is interested in values in several locations at various times. Much of the problem arises because of the complications associated with meteorological phenomena that involve changes in the radiative properties of the atmosphere and transport of heat energy from one geographic area to another. Consequently, for average values of radiation from the Earth, it is desirable to make use of meteorological studies pertaining to the heat balance of the Earth. One of the best of these studies was made by Baur and Philipps (1934, 1935). Tabulated values, principally from their study, will be presented here.

There are two parts to the problem of the Earth's heat balance: first, the relatively short-wavelength solar radiation; and second, the relatively long-wavelength thermal radiation from the Earth, including the atmosphere. Only a portion of the incident solar energy becomes involved in the Earth's heat budget because a substantial portion of the solar radiation is returned to space unused.

7.2. DISTRIBUTION OF SOLAR HEATING

The input of solar energy to the Earth is essentially a geometrical problem; however, the solid geometry of the situation is fairly complicated. List (1951) presented values for the average insolation incident on the Earth's atmosphere as a function of latitude and time of year. Values for the northern hemisphere are reproduced in Table 7-1. It must be remembered that these are values averaged over a period of a day or longer. To get values for a particular time, it would be necessary to construct the solar-altitude curve for the given latitude and time of year and to use this information to determine the variation throughout the day. Such a curve can be normalized using data from Table 7-1. Alternatively, the knowledge of the solar-altitude angle and the solar constant could be

TABLE 7-1

AVERAGE INSOLATION INCIDENT ON THE EARTH'S ATMOSPHERE

Latitude (°)	Average Insolation (w/cm²)			
	Jan	21 Mar	Jul	23 Sep
0–10	.0388	.0430	.0402	.0425
10–20	.0335	.0416	.0438	.0412
20–30	.0272	.0389	.0460	.0386
30–40	.0205	.0350	.0473	.0348
40–50	.0137	.0307	.0478	.0302
50–60	.0069	.0249	.0475	.0248
60–90	.0011	.0170	.0500	.0161

used to obtain instantaneous values for the incident radiation, in which case the solar constant must be corrected according to season to take into account the Earth's varying distance from the sun. This latter procedure was followed in preparing the data for Table 7-1, with integration of values over the period of a day to get the time-averaged values presented.

The solar radiation incident upon the Earth's atmosphere is partially absorbed by the atmosphere and the Earth's surface and partially reflected or scattered by the Earth's surface and atmosphere. The portion scattered and reflected back into space is generally referred to as albedo; unfortunately no tabulated values were given for this portion by Baur and Philipps (1934). However, they do give average values for the energy absorbed in the Earth's atmosphere and at the Earth's surface. These data are presented in Table 7-2.

The albedo is that portion of the incident radiation that is reflected to space

TABLE 7-2

AVERAGE SHORT-WAVE-ENERGY ABSORPTION

Latitude (°)	Energy Absorbed by Atmosphere (w/cm²)				Energy Absorbed by Earth's Surface (w/cm²)			
	Jan	21 Mar	Jul	23 Sep	Jan	21 Mar	Jul	23 Sep
0–10	0.0066	0.0071	0.0077	0.0076	0.0174	0.0193	0.0160	0.0179
10–20	0.0052	0.0062	0.0081	0.0071	0.0165	0.0207	0.0165	0.0168
20–30	0.0039	0.0054	0.0075	0.0060	0.0132	0.0190	0.0205	0.0186
30–40	0.0028	0.0046	0.0069	0.0050	0.0090	0.0158	0.0220	0.0171
40–50	0.0019	0.0038	0.0069	0.0043	0.0052	0.0123	0.0189	0.0130
50–60	0.0009	0.0029	0.0067	0.0036	0.0025	0.0095	0.0168	0.0091
60–90	0.0001	0.0018	0.0078	0.0027	0.0002	0.0047	0.0160	0.0047

without absorption. Average values for particular latitudes and seasons can be obtained by subtracting the absorbed radiation (Table 7-2) from the incident insolation (Table 7-1). Values determined in this manner are presented in Table 7-3. As with Table 7-1, the explicit time dependence through the course of the day is not shown or readily available in tabular form. To get these values it would be necessary to make some assumption such as that the intensity of the returned solar radiation is proportional to the intensity of the incident solar radiation. In this case, one would have to determine the curves of solar altitude versus time of day for the region and time of year concerned. The intensity of solar radiation per unit area of Earth's surface would be proportional to the sine of the solar-altitude angle. Curves of sine of solar-altitude angle versus time of day could be normalized so that the areas under the curves agree with the values in Table 7-3; the curves then would represent the time variation of the returned solar radiation through the day, subject to the assumption mentioned above.

TABLE 7-3

AVERAGE SHORT-WAVE SOLAR ENERGY REFLECTED BY THE ATMOSPHERE AND EARTH

Latitude (°)	Short-Wave Energy Reflected (w/cm²)			
	Jan	21 Mar	Jul	23 Sep
0–10	0.0150	0.0156	0.0171	0.0165
10–20	0.0123	0.0144	0.0192	0.0165
20–30	0.0116	0.0145	0.0161	0.0143
30–40	0.0101	0.0136	0.0152	0.0129
40–50	0.0075	0.0136	0.0183	0.0124
50–60	0.0043	0.0125	0.0206	0.0170
60–90	0.0017	0.0033	0.0224	0.0024

The worldwide and yearly average value of the albedo indicated by Table 7-3 is about 42 per cent; this value, based on the work of Baur and Philipps, is thought to be too large, mainly owing to their use of too high a value for cloud albedo. In more recent work, Fritz (1949) found a value of 35 per cent for the global albedo, and this value has been supported by a study by Houghton (1954), who found 34 per cent. Houghton's annual-average values are shown in **Fig. 7-1** as a function of latitude, along with the annual-average insolation at the top of the atmosphere (the long-wave radiation curve will be discussed below). Houghton did not present values for different seasons, so Baur and Philipps' data in Table 7-3 must be used to see the seasonal trends. However, in the annual mean, Houghton's data are considered to be the more accurate.

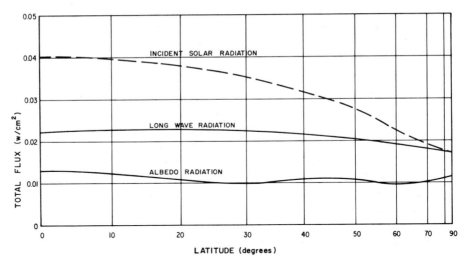

Fig. 7-1. Annual-average values of the albedo radiation and of the long-wavelength radiation emitted by the Earth and atmosphere, shown as functions of latitude. Also shown is the annual-average flux of solar energy incident upon the atmosphere.

7.3. THERMAL RADIATION FROM THE EARTH

The remaining part of the radiation from the Earth and atmosphere is the long-wavelength radiation. In considering the total radiation emitted by the Earth and atmosphere, it is not necessary to differentiate between that portion of the radiation originating at the Earth's surface and that portion originating within the Earth's atmosphere. Values for the total outgoing radiation are shown in Table 7-4 (Baur and Philipps, 1934). The values have been averaged over a period of a day or longer, and, while one would probably prefer to know the time dependence of this quantity throughout the day, the variation between the daytime and nighttime values can perhaps be ignored because it is not great.

Houghton's annual-average values for the long-wavelength radiation are shown in **Fig. 7-1**. As with the albedo radiation, Houghton's data are considered to be more accurate than Baur and Philipps' in terms of annual averages, but they do not show the seasonal trend that is indicated by Baur and Philipps' data.

All of the tabulated values except those for the solar insolation are apt to be highly variable. For example, water, which covers most of the Earth's surface, absorbs over 90 per cent of the incident solar radiation when the solar-altitude angle is above 25°. This absorption would lead to an extremely low albedo when the sky is very clear, whereas in the presence of extensive cloudiness about half of the incident solar radiation may be reflected, representing a change by a fac-

TABLE 7-4

TOTAL LONG-WAVE RADIATION FROM THE EARTH AND ATMOSPHERE

Latitude (°)	Long-Wave Energy Radiated (w/cm²)			
	Jan	21 Mar	Jul	23 Sep
0–10	0.0203	0.0212	0.0209	0.0206
10–20	0.0206	0.0210	0.0210	0.0211
20–30	0.0203	0.0204	0.0213	0.0213
30–40	0.0193	0.0194	0.0216	0.0213
40–50	0.0175	0.0175	0.0202	0.0201
50–60	0.0164	0.0164	0.0195	0.0185
60–90	0.0156	0.0152	0.0189	0.0177

tor of 5 or more from the extreme of no cloudiness. Similarly, in the case of the outgoing radiation from the Earth and atmosphere, one can imagine the extremes of dry and cloudless conditions and of extensive high-level cloudiness. In the former case there will be appreciable radiation from the Earth's surface at temperatures as high as +30 °C, while in the latter the source of the radiation may have a temperature as low as −55 °C.

Figure 7-2 shows schematically a typical spectral-radiance (i.e., intensity of

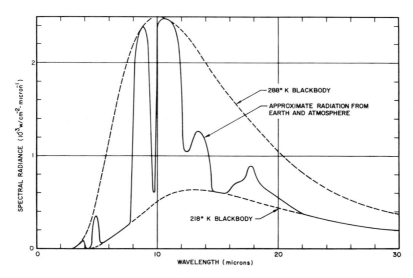

Fig. 7-2. Typical spectral-radiance curve for thermal radiation leaving the Earth. The 288 °K blackbody curve approximates the radiation from the Earth's surface, and the 218 °K blackbody curve approximates the radiation from the atmosphere in those spectral regions where the atmosphere is opaque.

emission per unit area per unit wavelength) curve for the radiation emitted by the Earth and its atmosphere. The upper blackbody curve represents radiation from the Earth's surface when the surface temperature is 288 °K. In spectral regions where the atmosphere is transparent, the radiation from the Earth's surface escapes into space. In spectral regions where the Earth's atmosphere is very opaque, the escaping radiation comes from the stratospheric region of the atmosphere, where a temperature of 218 °K is frequently representative (lower blackbody curve). In spectral regions where the atmospheric transparency is intermediate, the radiation to space falls between the two blackbody curves, as illustrated by the solid curve. It must be emphasized that **Fig. 7-2** is only illustrative of the problem, since there are many variables, and the actual atmospheric spectrum has a very complicated structure. The temperature of the Earth's surface varies with position and time, so that the 288° K value suggested in **Fig. 7-2** is only an average. The atmospheric transparency varies a great deal, principally because of varying amounts of water vapor if the air is clear and varying degrees and altitudes of cloudiness if the air is not clear. Although much more detailed and more accurate predictions than those shown in **Fig. 7-2** can be made for specific situations, observational data from satellites will be required before a good overall specification of the Earth's thermal-radiation environment can be given. Some such data have become available from Tiros satellites, but more data with more reliable energy scales are required.

7.4. AIRGLOW

Another type of atmospheric emission is known as the airglow, which is an emission in the visible, ultraviolet, and near-infrared portions of the spectrum. Since such emissions cannot be thermally excited at the temperatures occurring in the atmosphere, some other source of excitation is required. During the daytime and at twilight, absorption of solar radiation is probably the main source. However, the airglow continues through the night. Excited states with lifetimes long enough to account for emission throughout the night do not constitute an adequate explanation. Although the source of the night-airglow excitation is not known, it is probably chemical energy released in the recombination of atomic species into molecules.

The intensity of the night airglow is relatively weak, although it can easily be noted on a clear moonless night by holding one's hand overhead. The area covered by one's hand is clearly darker than the region between the stars; this difference is due to the airglow. Among the prominent emissions from the night sky are those of atomic oxygen at 5577 and 6300 A, sodium at 5893 A, molecular oxygen in the near ultraviolet, and hydroxyl radicals mainly in the near infrared. The emissions originate principally in the region between 80 and 100 km, where most of the recombination of atoms occurs. A notable exception to this is the oxygen 6300 A radiation, which originates at a considerably higher altitude. It is common practice to express the intensity of the emissions in terms of rayleighs, where 1 rayleigh equals 10^6 photons emitted per second in a square-centimeter column extending up through the atmosphere. The oxygen green line at 5577 A generally falls within a factor of 3 of 200 rayleighs, and the oxygen red line at 6300 A within a factor of 5 of 100 rayleighs. The molecular-oxygen Hertzberg bands in the near ultraviolet amount to about 150 rayleighs, and the hydroxyl-radical emission is about 7×10^6 rayleighs. A review of the night airglow has been given by Bates (1960), and a good book on the subject has been written by Chamberlain (1961).

REFERENCES

Bates, D. R. 1960. "The Airglow," in J. A. Ratcliffe, ed., *Physics of the Upper Atmosphere.* Academic Press, New York, pp. 219–67.

Baur, F., and H. Philipps. 1934. "Der Wärmehaushalt der Lufthülle der Nordhalbkugel in Januar und Juli und zur Zeit der Äquinoktien und Solstitien. Pt. I. Die Einstrahlung bei normaler Solarkonstante," *Gerlands Beitr. Geophys.,* **42,** 160–207.

Baur, F., and H. Philipps. 1935. "Der Wärmehaushalt der Lufthülle der Nordhalbkugel in Januar und Juli und zur Zeit der Äquinoktien und Solstitien. Pt. II. Ausstrahlung, Gegenstrahlung und meridionaler Wärmetransport bei normaler Solarkonstante," *Gerlands Beitr. Geophys.,* **45,** 82–132.

Chamberlain, J. W. 1961. *Physics of the Aurora and Airglow.* Academic Press, New York.

Fritz, S. 1949. "The Albedo of the Planet Earth and of Clouds," *J. Meteor.,* **6,** 277–82.

Houghton, H. G. 1954. "On the Annual Heat Balance of the Northern Hemisphere," *J. Meteor.,* **11,** 1–9.

List, R. J. 1951. *Smithsonian Meteorological Tables,* 6th ed. Smithsonian Institution, Washington, D.C.

8. Geomagnetism

A. J. Dessler

Department of Space Science,
Rice University, Houston, Texas

8. Geomagnetism

A. J. Dessler

Department of Space Science,
Rice University, Houston, Texas

8.1. INTRODUCTION

The gross features of the geomagnetic field are similar to those of a uniformly magnetized sphere. However, in detail, such a simple model is inadequate. There are many irregularities that cause deviations from a smooth dipole field. Aside from the irregularities, the axis which would represent the axis of magnetization of the Earth does not pass through the Earth's center but is eccentric. In addition, the geomagnetic field varies continuously in an irregular manner.

The Earth's main magnetic field is commonly supposed to originate by dynamo action in the fluid motion of the molten metallic core of the Earth (Elsasser, 1950). This fluid motion is unsteady; it changes slightly from year to year and produces the secular variation, which requires hundreds of years to produce a significant change in the geomagnetic field. Transient variations, which take place in times less than one year (some occurring in a small fraction of a second), are produced chiefly by the interaction between solar plasma and the geomagnetic field.

Scientific observations of the geomagnetic field have been made for the past several hundred years. For example, the secular variation was discovered in 1635, by means of data obtained as early as 1580. The transient variations were discovered in 1722. The first magnetic observatories were constructed during the late eighteenth century for the purpose of making systematic observations over widely separated geographic positions. Since that time enormous amounts of data have been gathered. An outstanding job of describing, summarizing, and analyzing the data to 1940 may be found in *Geomagnetism* by Chapman and Bartels (1940).

Research since 1940 has been directed mainly toward an understanding of the transient variations. The greatest progress in this direction has come about through applications of the principles of hydromagnetism. In an early paper based on these principles, Parker (1956) pointed out that, "The high electrical conductivity of the region surrounding Earth, inferred from the observations of atmospheric whistlers and the zodiacal light, requires abandoning the customary models for producing geomagnetic (transient variations). . . . It becomes necessary to adopt a purely hydromagnetic approach wherein one focuses his attention only on the magnetic lines of force of the geomagnetic field and their displacement with the conducting gas surrounding Earth."

A review of geomagnetism is presented in this chapter. Sections 8.2, 8.3, and 8.4 contain descriptions of the spherical harmonic analysis and other static magnetic-field parameters. Transient variations are discussed in Section 8.5.

8.2. MAIN GEOMAGNETIC FIELD

The geomagnetic field is quantitatively described in terms of magnetic elements that specify the strength and orientation of the field at the Earth's surface. There are several sets of elements which can be used for this purpose—the most commonly used ones are listed in Table 8-1. Occasionally X, Y, and Z are used for the magnetic elements; X and Y are respectively the north and east components of H, and these directions define the positive values; i.e., the south and west components are negative and Z is the same as V.

TABLE 8-1

Magnetic Elements

Element	Description
F	Total magnetic intensity
I	Inclination or magnetic dip; defined as the smallest angle between the horizontal and the direction of the magnetic-field vector; positive in regions where the north-seeking end of a freely suspended magnetized needle points downward; thus magnetic dip is positive over most of the northern hemisphere
D	Magnetic variation or declination, defined as the angle between true north and the magnetic north indicated by a compass; positive when the magnetic north is to the east of true north
H	Intensity of the horizontal component of the geomagnetic field; always positive
V	Intensity of the vertical component of the geomagnetic field; has the same sign as I

Figures 8-1 through 8-7 represent the best present knowledge of the main field over the surface of the Earth, taken from Hydrographic Office charts, which are published every five years (Air Force Geophysics Research Directorate, 1960). The total intensity F, the horizontal intensity H, the vertical intensity Z, the declination D, and the inclination I are shown. The secular change,

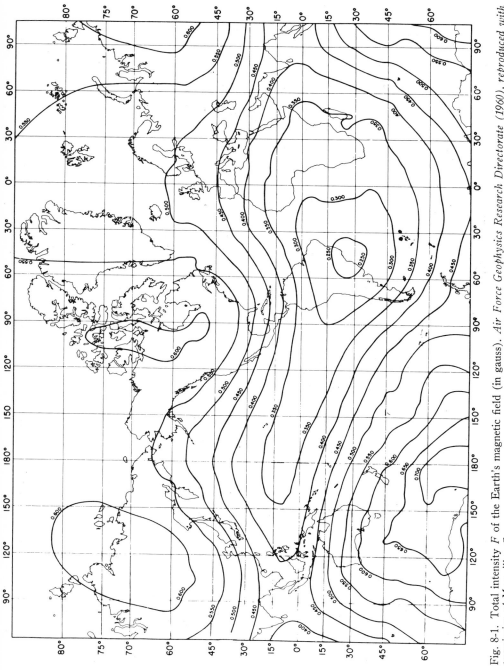

Fig. 8-1. Total intensity F of the Earth's magnetic field (in gauss). *Air Force Geophysics Research Directorate (1960), reproduced with permission of Macmillan Co.*

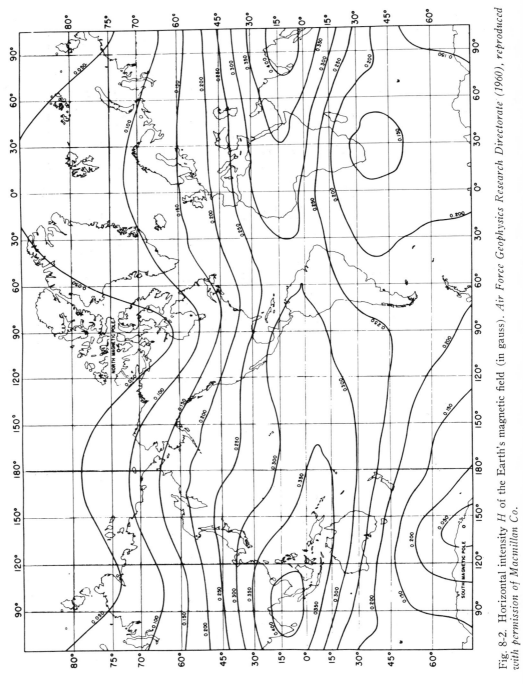

Fig. 8-2. Horizontal intensity H of the Earth's magnetic field (in gauss). *Air Force Geophysics Research Directorate (1960), reproduced with permission of Macmillan Co.*

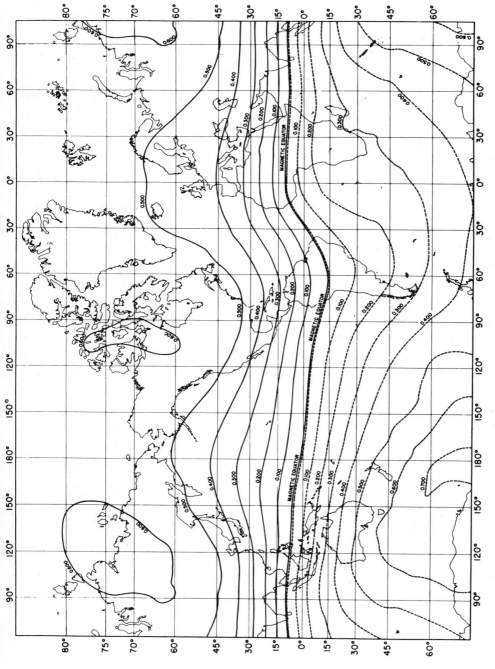

Fig. 8-3. Vertical intensity Z of the Earth's magnetic field (in gauss). Full lines designate the vertical intensity over areas of positive dip; dashed lines, areas of negative dip. *Air Force Geophysics Research Directorate (1960), reproduced with permission of Macmillan Co.*

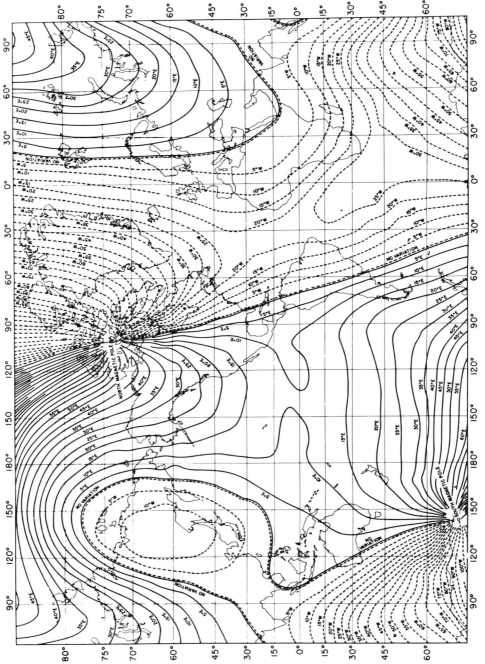

Fig. 8-4. Declination D of the Earth's magnetic field. Isogonic lines denote the variation or magnetic declination in degrees; full lines designate easterly (positive) variation, dashed lines westerly (negative) variation. *Air Force Geophysics Research Directorate (1960), reproduced with permission of Macmillan Co.*

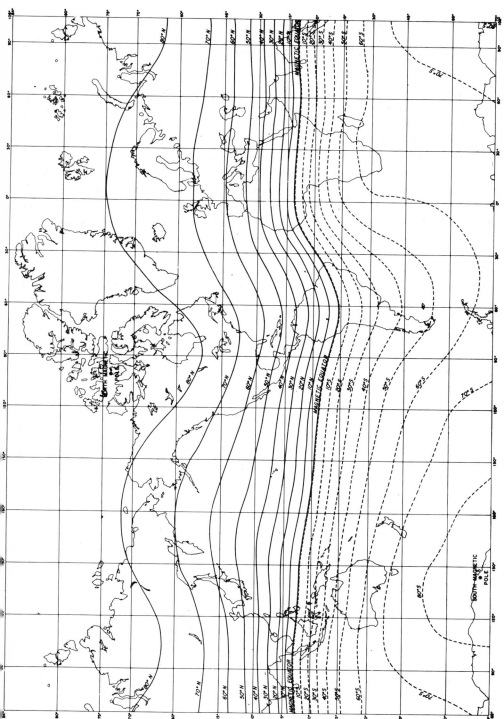

Fig. 8-5. Inclination, or dip I, of the Earth's magnetic field. Isoclinic lines denote magnetic inclination or dip in degrees.

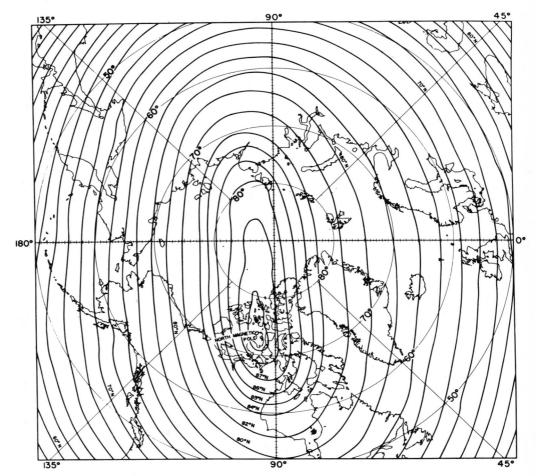

Fig. 8-6. Inclination or dip *I* of the Earth's magnetic field for the north-polar area. Isoclinic lines denote magnetic inclination or dip in degrees. *Air Force Geophysics Research Directorate (1960), reproduced with permission of Macmillan Co.*

which amounts to about 0.1 per cent of the total field per year, can be found on charts prepared by the Hydrographic Office in the 1700 series. The accuracy of the main field charts reproduced in this chapter depends on how well the various parts of the Earth are surveyed magnetically. In the United States and in Europe, the charts are probably accurate within 0.1 per cent, but at high latitudes and in other less accessible areas, the errors are considerably larger. Surface anomalies on the order of 1000 miles or less in extent do not appear on the charts. In some places, these local anomalies may constitute an important fraction of the total field.

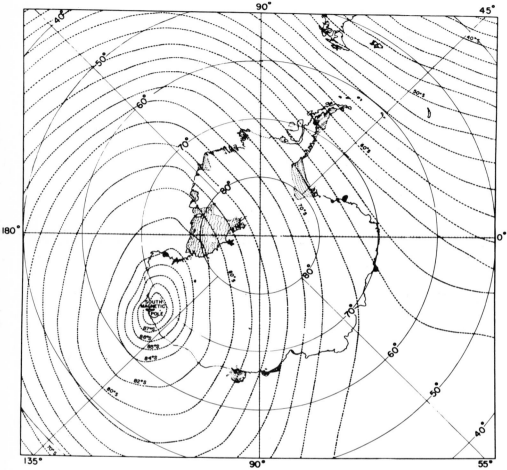

Fig. 8-7. Inclination or dip *I* of the Earth's magnetic field for the south-polar area. Isoclinic lines denote magnetic inclination or dip in degrees. *Air Force Geophysics Research Directorate (1960), reproduced with permission of Macmillan Co.*

8.3. SPHERICAL HARMONIC ANALYSIS OF MAIN FIELD

The first spherical harmonic analysis of the main geomagnetic field at the Earth's surface was made by Gauss in the nineteenth century. A number of authors, using improved data and varying numbers of coefficients, have performed harmonic analyses since then. The early works have been discussed by Chapman and Bartels (1940); more recent work has been done by Vestine *et al.* (1947), Finch and Leaton (1957), and Fougere (1964).

Assuming an internal origin for the geomagnetic field, we can derive the field from a potential of the form

$$V = a \sum_{n=1}^{\infty} \sum_{m=0}^{n} (a/r)^{n+1} \, (g_n{}^m \cos m\phi + h_n{}^m \sin m\phi) \, P_n{}^m \, (\cos \theta) \,,$$

$$(8\text{-}1)$$

where, in a right-handed system of geocentric spherical coordinates,

a is the radius of the Earth,
r is the distance to the field point from the Earth's center.
θ is the geographic co-latitude (i.e., polar angle),
ϕ is the east longitude,
$P_n{}^m \, (\cos \theta)$ is a multiple of the normalized associated Legendre polynomial of degree n and order m, and
$g_n{}^m$ and $h_n{}^m$ are the gaussian coefficients determined from the surface magnetic data.

The factor by which the normalized associated Legendre polynomial is multiplied is

$$\sqrt{\frac{2n+1}{2}} \quad \text{for} \;\; m = 0 \,,$$

$$\frac{\sqrt{2n+1}}{2} \quad \text{for} \;\; m \geq 1 \,.$$

The gradient of the potential function gives the magnetic-field components that are observed at the Earth's surface $(r = a)$; i.e.,

$$X = \frac{1}{r} \frac{\partial V}{\partial \theta} \,, \quad Y = -\frac{1}{r \sin \theta} \frac{\partial V}{\partial \phi} \,, \quad Z = \frac{\partial V}{\partial r} \,. \qquad (8\text{-}2)$$

The most widely used harmonic analysis is that derived by Finch and Leaton (1957). Their gaussian coefficients, which have the same physical dimensions as the magnetic field intensity, are presented in Table 8-2. The field described by these coefficients represents the gross features of the surface field to within about 1 per cent. A discussion of 11 different published sets of gaussian coefficients derived by various authors to describe the geomagnetic field for the epochs 1955.0 to 1960.0 is given by Fougere (1964). He concludes that the best harmonic analyses describe the Earth's field to about 1 per cent, while the worst has an accuracy of about 6 per cent.

TABLE 8-2

Gaussian Coefficients g_n^m and h_n^m to $m = n = 6$, Epoch 1955.0,
in Gauss (Schmidt Normalization)
(Finch and Leaton, 1957)

g_1^0	−0.3055	g_2^2	+0.0158	g_4^4	+0.0031
g_2^0	−0.0152	g_3^2	+0.0126	g_5^4	−0.0015
g_3^0	+0.0118	g_4^2	+0.0058	g_6^4	−0.0003
g_4^0	+0.0095	g_5^2	+0.0020		
g_5^0	−0.0027	g_6^2	+0.0002		
g_6^0	+0.0010			h_4^4	−0.0017
		h_2^2	+0.0024	h_5^4	−0.0014
g_1^1	−0.0227	h_3^2	+0.0029	h_6^4	−0.0001
g_2^1	+0.0303	h_4^2	−0.0031		
g_3^1	−0.0191	h_5^2	+0.0010	g_5^5	−0.0007
g_4^1	+0.0080	h_6^2	+0.0011	g_6^5	0.0000
g_5^1	+0.0032				
g_6^1	+0.0005	g_3^3	+0.0091		
		g_4^3	−0.0038	h_5^5	+0.0009
		g_5^3	−0.0004	h_6^5	−0.0003
h_1^1	+0.0590	g_6^3	−0.0024		
h_2^1	−0.0190				
h_3^1	−0.0045	h_3^3	−0.0009	g_6^6	−0.0011
h_4^1	+0.0015	h_4^3	−0.0004		
h_5^1	+0.0002	h_5^3	−0.0005		
h_6^1	−0.0002	h_6^3	0.0000	h_6^6	−0.0001

Sets of harmonic coefficients that represent the deformation of the outer part of the geomagnetic field by the solar wind—i.e., an external contribution to the geomagnetic field—have been derived by Mead (1964) and Midgley (1964).

Equations for deriving the position of a single centered or eccentric dipole which represents a reasonable approximation to the geomagnetic field have been given by Bartels (1936). A first approximation to the Earth's magnetic field corresponds to a magnetic dipole situated at the geographic center of the Earth and inclined at an angle of 11° to the geographic axis. The axis of the centered dipole intersects the surface of the Earth and defines the geomagnetic poles. Hence, it also defines the geomagnetic coordinate system. **Figure 8-8** shows the geomagnetic coordinate system superimposed on a Mercator projection in geographic coordinates according to Vestine *et al.* (1948). The geomagnetic poles are not the same as the magnetic poles that are indicated on magnetic-field maps. These latter poles are usually the dip poles, which are the points on the Earth's surface where the magnetic field is vertical. Thus the magnetic poles shown in **Figs. 8-6** and **8-7** are dip poles and are not coincident with the geomagnetic poles, which are derived from the centered-dipole approximation.

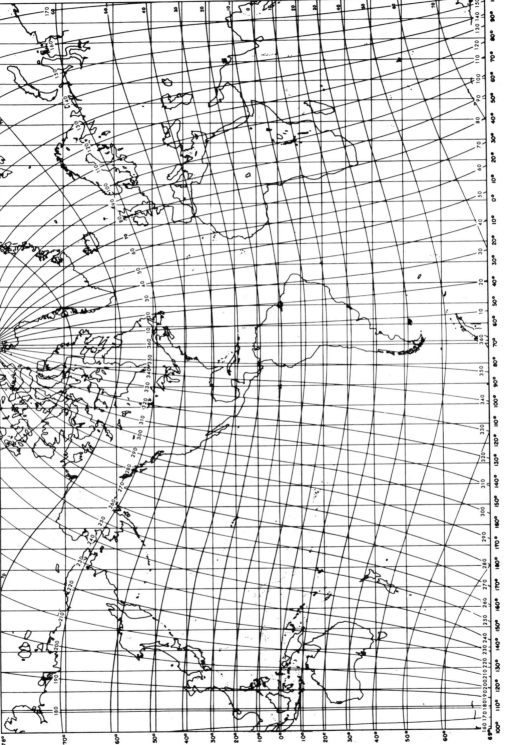

Fig. 8-8. Geomagnetic dipole field coordinate grid (curved lines) superimposed on a Mercator projection of the world.

An improved approximation to the observed geomagnetic field is provided by a dipole located at the magnetic center of the Earth (the eccentric dipole). The position of the eccentric dipole has been determined by Parkinson and Cleary (1958) from the harmonic analysis of Finch and Leaton (1957). The location and orientation of the eccentric dipole for the epoch 1955.0 is given in the following quotation from Parkinson and Cleary (1958):

> The eccentric dipole is displaced by 0.0685 Earth radii (about 436 km) from the center towards a point at latitude 15.6° N, longitude 150.9° E (just east of the Marianas). This is 6.6°, or 730 km north of the geomagnetic equator. The poles of the eccentric dipole (i.e., the points where its axis cuts the surface of the Earth) are at 81.0° N, 84.7° W and at 75.0° S, 120.4° E (i.e., in Ellesmere Is. and in Wilkes Land). The axis of the eccentric dipole is not vertical at these points, but is inclined at 3.9° to the vertical in the direction of the corresponding geomagnetic pole. . . . The field of the eccentric dipole is, of course, parallel to its axis, and so it also is inclined to the vertical at the poles of the eccentric dipole. The eccentric dipole field is vertical at two points which are further from the geomagnetic poles. The positions of these points are 82.4° N, 137.3° W and 67.9° S, 130.6° E.

The approximate geographic locations of the various magnetic poles are summarized in Table 8-3.

TABLE 8-3

GEOGRAPHIC LATITUDE AND LONGITUDE OF THE MAGNETIC DIP POLES

As defined by	Northern Hemisphere	Southern Hemisphere
Observed Field	74° N, 259° E	68° S, 144° E
Centered Dipole (Geomagnetic Poles)	79° N, 291° E	79° S, 111° E
Eccentric Dipole	82° N, 223° E	68° S, 131° E

The geomagnetic coordinate system (based on the centered-dipole approximation) has only limited usefulness in analyzing phenomena that are geomagnetically controlled, e.g., aurora and the geographical distribution of the Van Allen radiation. The centered-dipole model is a crude, first-order approximation to the geomagnetic field; hence, it is not surprising to find errors of several degrees in the predicted location of geomagnetically related regions.

A more useful magnetic parameter is the magnetic or dip latitude. which can be obtained from the relationship between latitude and dip angle for a perfect dipole,

$$\lambda_m = \text{Arc tan} \left[\tfrac{1}{2} \tan I \right],$$

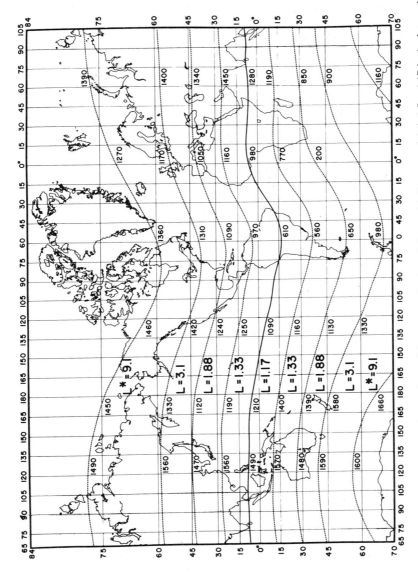

Fig. 8-9. Integral-invariant traces superimposed on a Mercator projection of the world. The trace labeled $L = 1.17$ is the integral-invariant equator and may be considered the best approximation to the magnetic equator. Altitudes (in kilometers) to arbitrarily selected field values of 0.20, 0.22, 0.28, 0.30, and 0.32 gauss are given at 60° intervals along magnetically conjugate pairs of traces, which are labeled with their respective L values. These altitudes show the displacement of the Earth's magnetic center from the geographic center.

where λ_m is the magnetic or dip latitude, and I is the observed magnetic inclination or dip. When applied to the Earth's magnetic field, this formula is empirically found to give a better fit than geomagnetic coordinates to the geographic distribution of geomagnetically controlled phenomena.

An even better description of the geomagnetic field, and one more physically meaningful, is based on the integral invariant, described in Section 3.2.1. By means of the integral invariant, the path or trace of the mirror point of a particle trapped in the geomagnetic field can be described analytically. **Figure 8-9** outlines a coordinate system based on the calculations of Jensen *et al.* (1960). Trace $L = 1.17$ is the integral-invariant equator. The altitude to a fixed magnetic-field value is given in kilometers along each integral-invariant trace for the case where the magnetic-field value was arbitrarily chosen to be that near 1500 km at 120° E longitude. The altitudes elsewhere are then defined by the integral invariant. This figure shows very nicely the displacement of the eccentric dipole derived by Parkinson and Cleary (1958). The traces are in pairs that are connected by a given L value. The L value may be thought of as approximately the distance from the magnetic center of the Earth to the equatorial crossing of the integral-invariant shell.

Sometimes in the literature one sees L values converted into integral-invariant latitudes by means of the dipole relationship

$$L \cos^2 \lambda_I = 1, \text{ or } \lambda_I = \text{Arc cos } L^{-1/2} .$$

This transformation is inaccurate and, therefore, either should not be used at all or should be used with great caution. First, O'Brien (1963) has shown that above about $L = 6$, L loses its physical significance. This is rather to be expected, since the L values are calculated from the spherical harmonic analysis that is based on the assumption that there is no external contribution to the geomagnetic field. Deformation of the geomagnetic field by the solar wind, as illustrated in **Fig. 8-14**, must have a significant effect at large L values. Second, as may be seen by comparing **Fig. 3-6** with **Fig. 8-5**, the dip equator does not correspond to $L = 1$ (in fact, $L = 1$ does not give an equator-like contour). Likewise, $L = 2$, which should correspond to 45° latitude, is significantly different from the 63.5° dip line that corresponds to a dip magnetic latitude of 45°.

8.4. MAIN FIELD ABOVE THE EARTH

Vestine *et al.* (1947) indicate that at least 99 per cent of the main magnetic field at the surface of the Earth originates from sources within the Earth. When the magnetic field is known at all points on a closed surface that encompasses the sources of the field, the field is completely determined at all points outside the surface. The potential of the main field, given in Eq. (8-1), may be expressed in the form

$$V = \sum_{n=1}^{\infty} \frac{a^{n+2}}{r^{n+1}} T_n ,$$ (8-3)

where

$$T_n = \sum_{m=0}^{n} (g_n^m \cos m\phi + h_n^m \sin m\phi) P_n^m(\cos \theta) .$$ (8-4)

The field at the surface $r = a$ is determined by g_n^m and h_n^m. In order to compute the field at an altitude h above the Earth, let $a_1 = a + h$; then V may be written in the convenient form

$$V = \sum_{n=1}^{\infty} \frac{a_1^{n+2}}{r^{n+1}} T_n \left(\frac{a}{a_1}\right)^{n+2} .$$ (8-5)

It is seen that the gauss coefficients of degree n are diminished in the ratio $(a/a_1)^{n+2}$ at altitude h. Local anomalies which correspond to harmonics of much higher degree are thus reduced effectively with elevation. The intensity of the dipole field and its components decreases outward as the cube of the distance from the center of the Earth. The contributions to the geomagnetic field of harmonic terms of $n = 2, 3, 4, 5$, and so on decrease outward proportional to r^{-4}, r^{-5}, r^{-6}, and r^{-7}, respectively. Consequently, the greater the distance from the Earth, the more dipolar is the permanent field; contributions to field variations by sheet currents or ring currents are excluded from consideration for the present. It may be anticipated that the fit between the observed and the computed values of the permanent field will be better at altitude h than at the Earth's surface, since a limited number of terms cannot represent accurately the fine detail of the anomalies in the surface field.

The 48-term harmonic analysis of the geomagnetic field has been used by Vestine and Sibley (private communication) to calculate the field distribution around the Earth. Some of the results of these calculations are shown in **Figs. 8-10** and **8-11**, where the altitudes of constant field strength of 0.010 gauss and the total field strength at 5000-km altitude are shown.

For various geophysical applications, it is of value to know the path of the lines of force of the geomagnetic field. Vestine and Sibley (1960) have computed the intersection with the Earth's surface of lines of force between the southern hemisphere and the northern hemisphere, based on the first 48 gauss coefficients. **Figure 8-12** represents the results of their calculations.

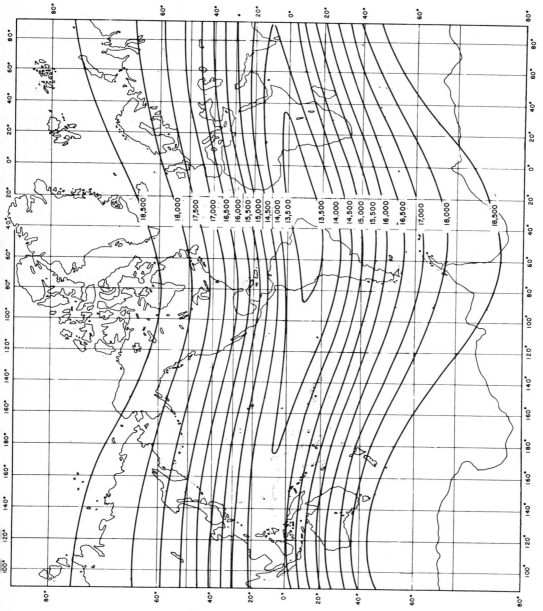

Fig. 8-10. Altitudes (in kilometers) to the surface of constant total field $F = 0.01$ gauss.

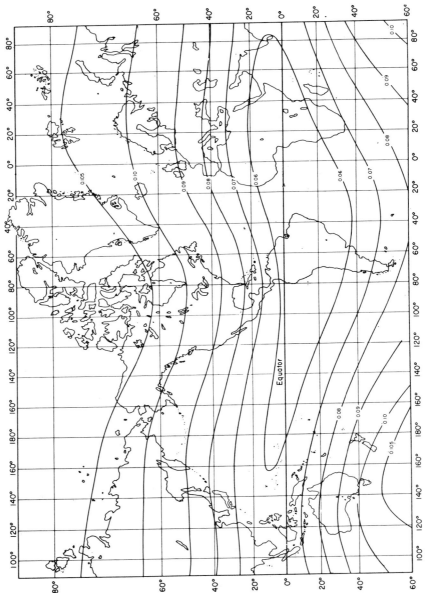

Fig. 8-11. Contours of total field strength F (in gauss) at 5000-km altitude.

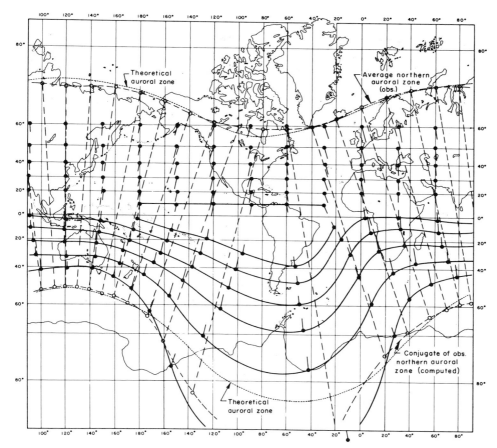

Fig. 8-12. Approximate intersections of lines of force of the geomagnetic field with the Earth's surface in the northern and southern hemispheres, based on the first 48 gauss coefficients. The points of intersection are shown by dots, associated in pairs; the short lines extending from the dots indicate the direction to the associated point. The association of points in the northern and southern auroral zones is also shown, but here the pairs are joined by dashed lines. *Vestine and Sibley (1960), reproduced with permission of J. Geophys. Research.*

8.5. VARIATIONS IN THE GEOMAGNETIC FIELD

The direction and magnitude of the Earth's magnetic field are constantly fluctuating, and these variations are recorded continuously at magnetic observatories distributed over the Earth. The variations in the Earth's magnetic field may be separated into two types: (1) secular variations, which are very slow, requiring hundreds of years to produce a change of a few per cent; and (2) transient variations, which disturb the field for periods ranging from a fraction of a second to a few years.

The secular variation is due to changes in the current system within the Earth's core. These changes usually amount to less than 0.1 per cent per year of the geomagnetic field over most of the Earth's surface. At any given location, the secular change is not a constant; rather, it changes in magnitude and occasionally in sign from year to year in such a way that hundreds of years are required to produce, for example, a 1 per cent change in the Earth's magnetic moment.

A useful measure of the transient geomagnetic activity recorded by observatory magnetometers is available in the form of the "three-hourly range index" or K index—a figure indicating the magnetic character over a given three-hour period. The K-index scale is defined for each observatory in terms of the amplitude of the magnetic variations during each three-hour period. This index varies from 0 to 9, with $K = 0$ indicating magnetic quiet or calm, while $K = 9$ signifies great fluctuations in the geomagnetic field.

The K index is further subdivided by means of the affixes $-$ and $+$, so that the indexes may be divided into thirds. Thus, 5+ means $5\frac{1}{3}$, 5o means 5, and 5− means $4\frac{2}{3}$. The K indexes are given for eight three-hour periods, starting with the period 0000-0300 Universal Time.

The K indexes from the individual observatories are combined into a worldwide or planetary index, K_p. The individual observatories furnishing the K indexes that are converted into K_p indexes, in order of decreasing geomagnetic latitude, are as follows:

Meanood, Canada	Wingst, Germany
Sitka, Alaska	Witteveen, Netherlands
Lerwick, Shetlands	Hartland, England
Eskdalemuir, Scotland	Agincourt, Canada
Lovö, Sweden	Fredericksburg, Virginia
Rude Skov, Denmark	Amberly, New Zealand

Note that, of the 12 observatories contributing to the K_p index, seven are contained within a relatively small geographic area in Western Europe. Since the K index for a given observatory shows a diurnal variation, a compensation factor must be introduced to allow for the nonuniform geographical distribution of observatories. As might be expected, this compensation cannot be done perfectly, and a small Universal Time diurnal variation is detectable in a 30-year sample of K_p data (Michel, 1964).

The K_p index is a quasi-logarithmic measure of the amplitude of geomagnetic disturbances. That is, an increase in the K_p index from, say, 1 to 2 involves only a small increase in the amplitude of the geomagnetic fluctuations, while an increase from 8 to 9 involves a major increase in the amplitude of the fluctuations.

Indexes that bear a linear relationship to the amplitude of geomagnetic disturbances have been introduced by Bartels (1962). These indexes are the A_p index and the a_p index. They are "derived indexes" in that they are derived from the K_p index and not from the primary geomagnetic data. The K_p data are, at present, derived from the actual observatory magnetograms. The K_p data can be converted into the a_p index by means of Table 8-4. **Figure 8-13** illustrates the quasi-logarithmic relationship between K_p and a_p.

TABLE 8-4

CONVERSION TABLE FROM K_p TO a_p

$K_p =$	0o	0+	1−	1o	1+	2−	2o	2+	3−	3o
$a_p =$	0	2	3	4	5	6	7	9	12	15
$K_p =$	3+	4−	4o	4+	5−	5o	5+	6−	6o	
$a_p =$	18	22	27	32	39	48	56	67	80	
$K_p =$	6+	7−	7o	7+	8−	8o	8+	9−	9o	
$a_p =$	94	111	132	154	179	207	236	300	400	

The A_p index is the average of the a_p index for one day. Note that A_p is the average of the linear a_p. One should not take the daily sum of the K_p indexes, divide by 8, and then attempt to convert to A_p by means of Table 8-4 or **Fig. 8-13**, since in one case one is taking the average of a logarithm, while in the other case one is taking the logarithm of an average. The final results are not necessarily equal.

The a_p index has a convenient physical significance: in mid-latitude stations, the range, ΔB, of the most disturbed magnetic element in γ during a three-hour period is $\sim 2a_p$; e.g., $\Delta B = \sim 90\gamma$ for $a_p = 45$, which corresponds to $K_p = 5o$.

A magnetic index occasionally seen in the older literature is the international character figure C_i or the daily planetary character figure C_p. The C_i index ranges from 0.0 (very quiet) to 2.0 (intense storm), while index C_p ranges between 0.0 and 2.4. These indexes give 24-hour measure of geomagnetic activity and hence are related to the A_p index. C_i data are available back to the year 1884.

The K_p data are sometimes presented graphically in a form that is usually referred to as "musical diagrams" because of their superficial resemblance to a sheet of music. A useful compilation of K_p, A_p, a_p, and C_p indexes for the years 1932 to 1961 has been compiled by Bartels (1962). A continuing source of these

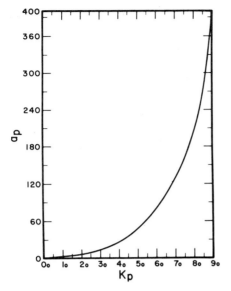

Fig. 8-13. The a_p index versus the K_p index (Bartels, 1962). The a_p has a convenient physical significance: in mid-latitude stations, the range, ΔB, of the most disturbed magnetic element in gamma during a three-hour period is $\sim 2a_p$, e.g., $\Delta B \approx 90\gamma$ for $a_p = 45$, which corresponds to $K_p = 5o$.

data is either the *Journal of Geophysical Research* or *"Solar-Geophysical Data, Part B,"* published by the National Bureau of Standards.

The transient variations in the geomagnetic field arise from changing electric currents flowing in the ionized regions of the atmosphere and/or from hydromagnetic waves generated by interactions between solar plasma and the geomagnetic field. Most of the transient variations are due to interactions between the geomagnetic field and ionized gas moving out from the sun. This gas, which on the average flows radially outward, is referred to as the solar wind (Parker, 1958). Direct evidence for the existence of a continuous solar wind comes from the comet-tail observations of Biermann (1953) and the plasma probe results of Mariner 2 (Snyder *et al.*, 1963). The solar wind will push into the geomagnetic field roughly to the point where the momentum flux of the solar wind is equal to the magnetic-field energy density (see Mead, 1964). By equating these two energy densities and assuming that the magnetic field strength at the magnetopause is given by

$$B = 2B_0(R_E/r)^3 \,,$$

where B_0 is the field strength at the Earth's surface, R_E is the radius of the Earth $(6.37 \times 10^8 \text{ cm})$, and r is the radial distance to the magnetopause, we obtain

$$r \approx R_E \left[\frac{B_0^2}{2\pi nmv^2} \right]^{1/6} . \qquad (8\text{-}6)$$

In cgs units, n is the number of solar-wind protons per cubic centimeter, m is their average mass in grams, and v is the solar-wind velocity in centimeters per second. Taking $B_0 = 0.35$ gauss, $n = 10$ protons (and electrons)/cm³, and $v = 5 \times 10^7$ cm/sec, we find that the solar wind will penetrate to $r = 8.7\ R_E$. These values for the solar-wind parameters are based on Mariner 2 results (Snyder *et al.,* 1963). The solar wind blowing against the geomagnetic field will probably distort the field into the shape shown in **Fig. 8-14**. The front surface is determined by the impact pressure of the solar wind. The length of the "tail" is not well determined. It has been argued that the tail is either closed relatively near the Earth by transverse thermal motion of the solar wind (Johnson, 1960) or is "open" for many Astronomical Units (Dessler, 1964).

The magnetosphere is generally defined as the region of space in which the geomagnetic field exerts a dominant influence on the motion of low-energy plasma and fast charged particles. In its usual sense, the magnetosphere is taken to be the region between the top of the ionospheric E region ($\sim$140 km altitude) and the outer boundary of the geomagnetic field (usually at distances greater than $\sim$10 R_E). The outer boundary of the magnetosphere, where there is a transition from geomagnetic to interplanetary field, is called the magnetopause; this surface is sketched in **Fig. 8-14**. The region between the magnetopause and the bow shock is here called the magnetosheath because of the spatial

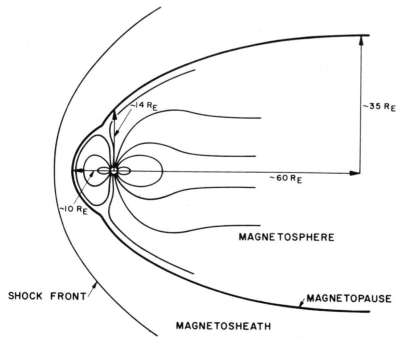

Fig. 8-14. Probable distortion of the geomagnetic field by the solar wind (cf. Mead, 1964, and Dessler, 1964).

similarity of this region to the ion sheath that surrounds meteors and re-entering space vehicles. This magnetosheath is also commonly referred to as the transition region. The magnetopause is probably stable (Dessler, 1961, 1962; Cahill and Amazeen, 1963) in the sense that it is a smooth, well defined surface, although the size of the magnetosphere may change with time (e.g., like a balloon).

As seen in **Fig. 8-14**, it is thought that a standing shock wave exists in front of the magnetosphere. The presence of this shock wave was postulated by Axford (1962) and Kellogg (1962). Experimental findings appear to be consistent with their hypothesis.

Hydromagnetic waves can be generated by changes in pressure on the geomagnetic field boundary when the density or velocity of the solar wind varies. These hydromagnetic waves can propagate through the geomagnetic field and may be observed at the Earth's surface as small fluctuations in the geomagnetic field. It is thought that the sudden-commencement phenomenon is transmitted from the magnetopause to the Earth's surface by hydromagnetic waves (Dessler *et al.*, 1960). A discussion of some of the more important features of the hydromagnetic-wave propagation through the geomagnetic field is given in Section 8.6.

It has been found by Walters (1964) that the presence of an oblique interplanetary magnetic field causes the standing shock wave to produce some asymmetry in the shape of the magnetosphere in the solar wind. As the interplanetary field direction varies, the shape of the magnetosphere will vary in concert. It is proposed by Dessler and Walters (1964) that the hydromagnetic waves, which are seen on the Earth's surface as geomagnetic disturbances, may be generated by changes in the direction of the interplanetary field through the changing asymmetry of the magnetosphere.

It has been shown by Snyder *et al.* (1963) from Mariner 2 data that a positive relationship exists between solar wind velocity and the daily sum of the geomagnetic index ΣK_p. They present an empirical relationship between the solar wind velocity V_s and ΣK_p: $V_s = 8.44 \, \Sigma K_p + 330$ (km/sec). The Mariner 2 results may also be presented in terms of the relationship, derived by Maer and Dessler (1964), between V_s and A_p: $V_s = 2.9 \times 10^2 A_p^{0.22}$ (km/sec). This relationship is plotted in **Fig. 8-15**.

Other observed transient variations are auroral-type fluctuations (Campbell, 1960); micropulsations and other extra-low frequency (ELF) phenomena, the cause of which, at present, is not understood (Benioff, 1960); diurnal variations, caused by tidal motions induced in the ionosphere by solar heating; seasonal variations, possibly due to changes in the conductivity of the ionosphere as a function of solar angle; an 11-year variation (in phase with the solar cycle), which is due either to changes in the total particle energy stored in the geomagnetic field or to variations in the pressure of the solar wind incident on the geomagnetic field.

The two most important transient variations are the diurnal variations and the fluctuations produced during geomagnetic storms by hydromagnetic waves. The diurnal variation is reasonably predictable for a given location and usually involves field changes of the order of 0.1 per cent of the total field. Except within a band near the integral-invariant equator, the diurnal variation is characterized by a minimum value for the field near local noon. Within the latitude range of about $\pm 10°$ of the integral-invariant equator, the sign of the variation is reversed, with the field showing an increase near local noon. The decrease at mid-latitude amounts to about 50 γ (1 $\gamma = 10^{-5}$ gauss), while the increase near the dip equator is approximately 100 γ in amplitude.

Geomagnetic storms are disturbances that occur in the magnetic field with a frequency varying with the solar cycle. The average characteristics of geomagnetic storms, as described by Chapman and Bartels (1940), are summarized in Table 8-5. Almost all magnetic storms display smoothed characteristics which fall within a factor of 3 of the numbers given in the table. A hydromagnetic model for geomagnetic storms based on the theory of Dessler and Parker (1959) provides an explanation of the causes of the observed phases; this theory is summarized in Table 8-5.

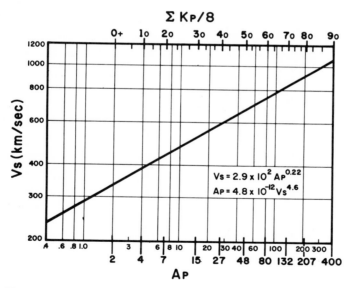

Fig. 8-15. Expected relationship between V_s and A_p or $\Sigma K_p/8$ (after Maer and Dessler, 1964; based on data of Snyder et al., 1963).

TABLE 8-5

GEOMAGNETIC STORMS

Features	Characteristics	Causes
Sudden Commencement	Horizontal component H of Earth's magnetic field increases in low and temperate latitudes; this increase, typically 20 to 30 γ, is largest at equatorial stations, with a rise time of 2 to 6 min.	Initiated by impact of solar plasma on geomagnetic field—sharp increase in strength of solar wind; effect of impact carried to lower ionosphere by hydromagnetic waves; sharp leading edge of solar plasma produced by weak magnetic field and plasma normally present in interplanetary space.
Initial Phase	H remains above normal undisturbed value (NUV) for 2 to 8 hr.	Increased solar-wind pressure on geomagnetic field; continues until solar-wind pressure relaxes.
Main Phase	H is farther below NUV than it was above NUV during Initial Phase; has decrease of 50 to 100 γ; after minimum is reached, H slowly recovers toward NUV, rate of recovery increasing with time—H-vs.-time curve is saucer shaped (d^2H/dt^2 is positive); phase lasts from 12 to 24 hr and tends to be noisy; large positive and negative excursions, with amplitudes of the order of several hundred gamma and periods of approximately $\frac{1}{3}$ hr, occur in magnetic field; these excursions are not shown in average magnetic-storm data.	Stresses set up by trapped protons in geomagnetic field; stress from both centrifugal force of trapped particles oscillating along lines of force through equatorial plane and from repulsion of magnetic moment of trapped particle by magnetic moment of Earth; large-amplitude fluctuations probably due to changes in solar-wind pressure and/or changes in the direction of interplanetary field.
Recovery Phase	Recovery is nearly exponential toward NUV (d^2H/dt^2 is negative); recovery time-constant between 1 and 3 days, although 10- to 20-day recovery time not uncommon; often no other magnetic disturbances occur during this phase.	Main-Phase stress relieved through transfer of energy of trapped protons to neutral hydrogen in geocorona by means of ion-atom charge-exchange process.

The main phase of magnetic storms is generally attributed to a ring current of energetic particles trapped in the geomagnetic field. The motion of such particles is described qualitatively in Section 3.2.1.

8.6. HYDROMAGNETIC-WAVE PROPAGATION

Hydromagnetic waves are simply a form of electromagnetic wave appropriate to the medium in which they propagate. This fact is clear from the derivation in which hydromagnetic-wave propagation follows from Maxwell's equations (Alfvén, 1950, p. 84). Thus hydromagnetic waves are subject to the same laws of reflection, refraction, and absorption as any other electromagnetic wave, with some modifications imposed in certain cases by a particular mode of propagation (e.g., Karplus, 1960).

For conditions applicable to the Earth's outer ionosphere, the hydromagnetic wave velocity is given by

$$V_{hm} = B/(4\pi\rho)^{1/2} ,$$

where ρ is the mass density of the ionized component in g/cm³. The velocity of

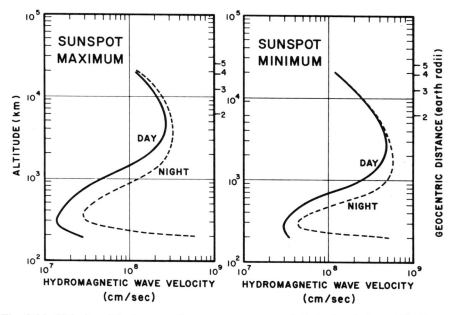

Fig. 8-16. Velocity of hydromagnetic waves at a magnetic latitude of about 30°. These curves apply for both longitudinal and transverse waves; i.e., both along the magnetic field and perpendicular to it.

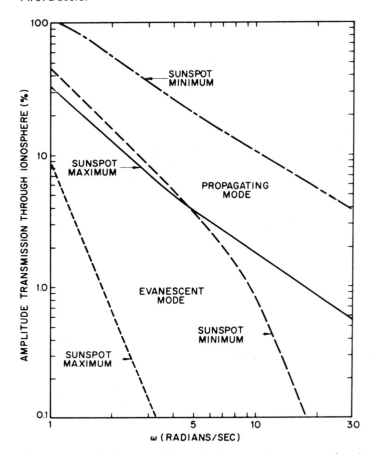

Fig. 8-17. Fractional amplitude transmission of hydromagnetic waves passing through the ionosphere versus incident angular frequency. Karplus, Francis, and Dragt (1962).

hydromagnetic waves propagating at latitude $\pm 30°$ versus altitude is shown in **Fig. 8-16**. This curve applies for both longitudinal and transverse waves. The ion-density values given in Chapter 2 were adopted in calculating this curve.

As shown in **Fig. 8-16**, the hydromagnetic wave velocity in the magnetosphere is in the range 10^{-2} to 10^{-3} of the velocity of light. Thus, a significant time should elapse between the observation of a magnetic impulse near the front of the magnetosphere and its arrival at the Earth's surface. The hydromagnetic wave transit time for a wave propagating from various geocentric distances to the Earth's surface is shown in Table 8-6. These times were calculated, using the velocity curves of **Fig. 8-16**.

The attenuation and dissipation of energy of hydromagnetic waves passing

TABLE 8-6

HYDROMAGNETIC WAVE PROPAGATION TIME

Geocentric Distance (Earth Radii)	Time of Propagation to Earth's Surface (Seconds)			
	Sunspot Maximum		Sunspot Minimum	
	Day	Night	Day	Night
8	49	45	47	46
7	36	32	33	32
6	26	22	23	22
5	18	14	14	13
4	13	9.4	8.8	8.0
3	9.4	6.0	4.6	3.9
2	6.4	3.4	2.5	1.8

through the ionosphere have been studied by Karplus *et al.* (1962). The fraction of the incident-wave amplitude which passes through the ionosphere versus wave frequency is shown in **Fig. 8-17.**

REFERENCES

Air Force Geophysics Research Directorate. 1960. *Handbook of Geophysics.* Macmillan Co., New York, pp. 10-1 to 10-68.

Alfvén, H. 1950. *Cosmical Electrodynamics.* Oxford University Press, London.

Axford, W. I. 1962. "The Interaction Between the Solar Wind and the Earth's Magnetosphere," *J. Geophys. Research,* **67,** 3791–96.

Bartels, J. 1936. "The Eccentric Dipole Approximating the Earth's Magnetic Field," *Terr. Mag.,* **41,** 225–50.

Bartels, J. 1962. "Collection of Geomagnetic Planetary Indexes K_p and Derived Daily Indexes A_p and C_p for the Years 1932 to 1961," *IAGA Bulletin No. 18* (North-Holland, Amsterdam).

Benioff, Hugo. 1960. "Observations of Geomagnetic Fluctuations in the Period Range 0.3 to 120 Seconds," *J. Geophys. Research,* **65,** 1413–22.

Biermann, L. 1953. "Physical Processes in Comet Tails and Their Relation to Solar Activity," *Mémoires de la Société Royale des Sciences de Liége,* Vol. 13, 291–302.

Cahill, L. J., and P. G. Amazeen. 1963. "The Boundary of the Geomagnetic Field," *J. Geophys. Research,* **68,** 1835–43.

Campbell, W. H. 1960. "Magnetic Micropulsations and the Pulsating Aurora," *J. Geophys. Research,* **65,** 874.

Chapman, S., and J. Bartels. 1940. *Geomagnetism.* Oxford University Press, London.

Dessler, A. J. 1961. "The Stability of the Interface Between the Solar Wind and the Geomagnetic Field," *J. Geophys. Research,* **66,** 3587–90.

Dessler, A. J. 1962. "Further Comments on Stability of Interface Between Solar Wind and the Geomagnetic Field," *J. Geophys. Research,* **67,** 4892–94.

Dessler, A. J. 1964. "Length of Magnetospheric Tail," *J. Geophys. Research,* **69,** 3913–18.

Dessler, A. J., and E. N. Parker. 1959. "Hydromagnetic Theory of Geomagnetic Storms," *J. Geophys. Research,* **64,** 2239–52.

Dessler, A. J., W. E. Francis, and E. N. Parker. 1960. "Geomagnetic Storm Sudden Commencement Rise Times, *J. Geophys. Research*, **65**, 2715–19.

Dessler, A. J., and G. K. Walters. 1964. "Hydromagnetic Coupling Between Solar Wind and Magnetosphere," *Planet. Space Sci.*, **12**, 227–34.

Dungey, J. W. 1955. "Electrodynamics of the Outer Atmosphere," *The Physics of the Ionosphere*. The Physical Society, London, pp. 229–36.

Elsasser, W. M. 1950. "The Earth's Interior and Geomagnetism," *Revs. Modern Phys.*, **22**, 1–35.

Finch, H. F., and B. R. Leaton. 1957. "The Earth's Main Magnetic Field—Epoch 1955," *Monthly Notices, Roy. Astron. Soc., Geophysical Supplements*, **7**, 314–17.

Fougere, P. F. 1964. "Spherical Harmonic Analysis 2. A New Model Derived from Magnetic Observatory Data for Epoch 1960.0," submitted to *J. Geophys. Research*.

Jensen, D. C., R. W. Murray, and J. A. Welch, Jr. 1960. "Tables of Adiabatic Invariants for the Geomagnetic Field 1955.0." Air Force Special Weapons Center, Kirtland Air Force Base, New Mexico.

Johnson, F. S. 1960. "The Gross Character of the Geomagnetic Field in the Solar Wind," *J. Geophys. Research*, **65**, 3049–51.

Karplus, Robert. 1960. "Radiation of Hydromagnetic Waves," *Phys. Fluids*, **3**, 800–805.

Karplus, R., W. E. Francis, and A. J. Dragt. 1962. "The Attenuation of Hydromagnetic Waves in the Ionosphere," *Planet. Space Sci.*, **9**, 771–85.

Kellogg, P. J. 1962. "Flow of Plasma Around the Earth," *J. Geophys. Research*, **67**, 3805–11.

Maer, Kemp, Jr., and A. J. Dessler. 1964. "Comments on Paper by Conway W. Snyder, Marcia Neugebauer, and U. R. Rao, 'The Solar Wind Velocity and Its Correlation with Cosmic-Ray Variations and with Solar and Geomagnetic Activity,'" *J. Geophys. Research*, **69**, 2846.

Mead, G. D. 1964. "Deformation of the Geomagnetic Field by the Solar Wind," *J. Geophys. Research*, **67**, 1181–95.

Michel, F. C. 1964. "K_p as a Planetary Index," *J. Geophys. Research*, **69**, 4182–83.

Midgley, James E. 1964. "Perturbation of the Geomagnetic Field—A Spherical Harmonic Expansion," *J. Geophys. Research*, **69**, 1197–1200.

O'Brien, B. J. 1963. "A Large Diurnal Variation of the Geomagnetically Trapped Radiation," *J. Geophys. Research*, **68**, 989–95.

Parker, E. N. 1956. "On the Geomagnetic Storm Effect," *J. Geophys. Research*, **61**, 625–37.

Parker, E. N. 1958. "Interaction of the Solar Wind with the Geomagnetic Field," *Phys. Fluids*, **1**, 171–87.

Parkinson, W. D., and J. Cleary. 1958. "The Eccentric Geomagnetic Dipole," *Geophys. J.*, **1**, 346.

Snyder, C. W., M. Neugebauer, and U. R. Rao. 1963. "The Solar Wind Velocity and Its Correlation with Cosmic-Ray Variations and with Solar and Geomagnetic Activity," *J. Geophys. Research*, **68**, 6361–70.

Vestine, E. H., L. Laporte, I. Lange, and W. E. Scott. 1947. "The Geomagnetic Field, Its Description and Analysis." Publication No. 580, Carnegie Institution of Washington, Washington, D.C.

Vestine, E. H., L. Laporte, I. Lange, C. Cooper, and W. C. Hendrix. 1948. "Description of the Earth's Main Magnetic Field and Its Secular Change 1905–1945." Publication No. 578, Carnegie Institution of Washington, Washington, D.C.

Vestine, E. H., and W. L. Sibley. 1960. "The Geomagnetic Field in Space, Ring Currents, and Auroral Isochasms," *J. Geophys. Research*, **65**, 1967–79.

Walters, G. K. 1964. "Effect of Oblique Interplanetary Magnetic Field on Shape and Behavior of the Magnetosphere," *J. Geophys. Research*, **69**, 1769–83.

Appendix   Supplementary Data

SOLAR-SYSTEM DATA

Member of Solar System	Solar Distance Mean (A.U.)[e]	Solar Distance Mean (km)	Solar Distance Minimum (km)	Solar Distance Maximum (km)	Orbit Inclination	Orbit Eccentricity	Mean Radius (km)	Mass (g)
Mercury	0.387	5.79×10^7	4.59×10^7	6.97×10^7	7°00′	0.206	2.42×10^3	3.58×10^{26}
Venus	0.723	1.08×10^8	1.07×10^8	1.088×10^8	3°23′	0.007	6.16×10^3	4.90×10^{27}
Earth	1.000	1.49×10^8	1.458×10^8	1.520×10^8	0°00′	0.017	6.37×10^3	5.975×10^{27}
Mars	1.524	2.38×10^8	2.06×10^8	2.49×10^8	1°51′	0.093	3.33×10^3	6.58×10^{26}
Jupiter	5.203	7.78×10^8	6.39×10^8	8.14×10^8	1°18′	0.048	6.99×10^4	1.90×10^{29}
Saturn	9.539	1.426×10^9	1.344×10^9	1.502×10^9	2°29′	0.056	5.75×10^4	5.69×10^{28}
Moon	0.00258^a	3.84×10^{5a}	3.63×10^{5a}	4.04×10^{5a}	...	0.055	1.738×10^3	7.343×10^{25}
Sun	...	...	...	...	...	...	6.957×10^5	1.987×10^{33}

Member of Solar System	Visual Albedo	Surface Temperature (°K)	Density (g/cm³)	Surface Gravity[d]	Rotation Period	Sidereal Revolution Period (yr)	Mean Orbit Velocity (km/sec)	Escape Velocity (km/sec)
Mercury	0.058	690	6.2	0.30	88 d (?)	0.241	47.85	4.2
Venus	0.76	700	5.0	0.90	0.615 yr	0.615	35.01	10.3
Earth	0.39	288	5.52	1.00	23.93 hr	1.000	29.76	11.2
Mars	0.148	230	3.81	0.38	24.6 hr	1.88	24.11	5.0
Jupiter	0.51	135	1.36	2.65	9.9 hr	11.86	13.05	61
Saturn	0.50	120	0.72	1.14	10.2 hr	29.46	9.64	37
Moon	0.072	120–400	3.3	0.17	27.3 d	0.075	1.03^c	2.4
Sun	...	5800	1.41	27.9	27 d^b	...	...	620

[a] Distance from Earth.
[b] 24.65 near equator, increasing with latitude to 30.9 d at 60° and about 34 d near the poles.
[c] Velocity relative to Earth.
[d] Gravity relative to Earth.
[e] 1 A.U. = 1.4959882 × 10⁸ km.

185

CONVERSION FACTORS

Energy

1 ev = 1.6020×10^{-12} erg
1 joule = 10^7 ergs
1 hp-hr = 2.684×10^{13} ergs
1 kw-hr = 3.60×10^{13} ergs
1 ft-lb[a] = 1.3558×10^7 ergs
1 ft-poundal = 4.344×10^5 ergs
1 Btu = 1.0549×10^{10} ergs
1 calorie = 4.184×10^7 ergs
Wavelength associated with 1 ev, 12395 A
Frequency associated with 1 ev, 2.4186×10^{14} cps
Wave number associated with 1 ev, 8067.8
Temperature corresponding to 1 ev, 11606° K

Power

1 hp = 745.65w = 7.4565×10^9 ergs/sec
1 ft-lb[a]/sec = 1.3558 w = 1.3558×10^7 ergs/sec
1 w = 10^7 ergs/sec
1 Btu/sec = 1.0549×10^3 w = 1.0549×10^{10} ergs/sec
1 μw = 10^6 w = 10 ergs/sec

Mass

1 lb = 0.4536 kg = 453.6 g
1 slug = 32.174 lb = 1.4594×10^4 g

Pressure

1 psi[a] = 70.31 g[a]/cm² = 6.894×10^4 dyne/cm² = 51.71 mm Hg
1 lb[a]/ft² = 0.4882 g[a]/cm² = 4.788×10^2 dyne/cm² = 0.3591 mm Hg
1 g[a]/cm² = 980.6 dyne/cm² = 0.7355 mm Hg
1 dyne/cm² = 7.502×10^{-4} mm Hg

Force

1 poundal = 1.3825×10^4 dynes
1 pound-force[a] = 4.4481×10^5 dynes
1 newton = 10^5 dynes

Length

1 in. = 2.5400 cm
1 ft = 30.480 cm
1 yd = 91.440 cm
1 mile = 1.60935 km
1 nautical mile = 1.8532 km
1 μ = 10^{-4} cm
1 A = 10^{-8} cm

Temperature

To obtain °K from °C, add 273.16
To obtain °F from °C, multiply by 9/5 and add 32
To obtain °R from °K, multiply by 9/5

Electrical Units

1 coulomb = 2.998×10^9 statcoulomb = 0.1 abcoulomb
1 ampere = 2.998×10^9 statampere = 0.1 abampere
1 volt = 3.336×10^{-3} statvolt = 10^8 abvolt
1 ohm = 1.113×10^{-12} statohm = 10^9 abohm
1 farad = 8.988×10^{11} cm = 10^{-9} abfarad
1 henry = 1.113×10^{-12} stathenry = 10^9 cm
10^4 gauss = 1 weber/m²

[a] lb and g here are regarded as units of force, and the magnitudes of the forces are those exerted on unit masses by the Earth's sea-level gravitational field at 45° latitude.

USEFUL PHYSICAL CONSTANTS

Proton mass	1.67252×10^{-24} g
Electron mass	9.1091×10^{-28} g
Electronic charge	4.80298×10^{-10} esu
Rest-mass energy of proton	9.38256 Mev
Rest-mass energy of electron	0.511006 Mev
Cyclotron frequency of proton in 1-gauss field	1.525×10^{3} cps
Cyclotron frequency of electron in 1-gauss field	2.80×10^{6} cps
Velocity of 1-ev proton	1.385×10^{6} cm/sec
Velocity of 1-ev electron	5.931×10^{7} cm/sec
Avogadro number	6.02252×10^{23} particles/mole
Loschmidt number	2.68699×10^{19} particles/cm^3
Boltzmann constant (k)	1.38054×10^{-16} erg/deg
Planck constant (h)	6.6256×10^{-27} erg sec
Stefan-Boltzmann constant (σ)	5.6697×10^{-5} erg/cm^2-deg^4-sec
Wien displacement-law constant	2.8978×10^{-1} cm deg
Velocity of light (c)	2.997925×10^{10} cm/sec
Mechanical equivalent of heat	4.1840 joules/cal
Constant of gravitation (G)	6.670×10^{-8} dyne cm^2/g^2
Molar volume at STP	22.4136×10^{3} cm^3/mole
Gas constant per mole (R_0)	8.3143×10^{7} erg/mole-deg
Solar constant	0.140 watt/cm^2 ($= 2.00$ cal/cm^2-min)
Solar illuminance constant	13.67 lumens/cm^2
Visual magnitude of sun	-26.88
Standard atmospheric pressure	1.013250×10^{6} dyne/cm^2 (760 mm Hg)
Total mass of earth's atmosphere	5.14×10^{21} g
Density of air at STP	1.293×10^{-3} g/cm^3
Density of O_2 at STP	1.429×10^{-3} g/cm^3
Density of N_2 at STP	1.251×10^{-3} g/cm^3
Molecular weight of dry air	28.966
Specific heat of dry air at constant pressure (C_p)	0.240 cal/g-°K
constant volume (C_v)	0.171 cal/g-°K
Mean free path in air at STP	6.4×10^{-6} cm
Magnetic moment of Earth	8×10^{15} erg/gauss
Permeability of empty space (μ_0)	$4\pi \times 10^{-7}$ henry/m ($= 1.257 \times 10^{-6}$)
Permittivity of empty space (ε_0)	$10^{-9}/36\pi$ farad/m ($= 8.85 \times 10^{-12}$)
Velocity at which kinetic energy equals rest-mass energy	0.917 c
Acceleration of gravity at latitude λ	$978.05 \, (1 + 0.00529 \sin^2 \lambda)$ cm/sec^2 $= 980.6$ cm/sec^2 at $\lambda = 45°$

Index

Index